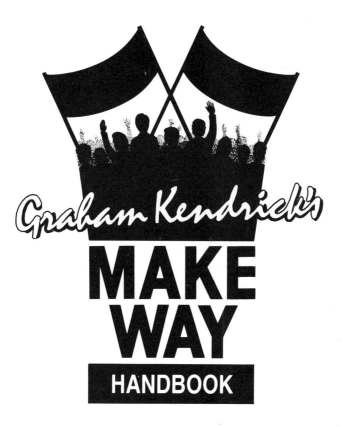

Graham Kendrick's MAKE WAY HANDBOOK

MUSIC EDITION

SONGS OF FELLOWSHIP

D1571764

KINGSWAY PUBLICATIONS
EASTBOURNE

MAKE WAY

ISBN 0 86065 659 4

*Compiled by Hilary Brand & Mark Kensington
with additional material from
Peter Brand, Jill Kendrick, Dave Liggins,
Jacky Males, Diana McKinnon, Mike Oakes,
Geoff Shearn, Jo Thomas and Graham Warner.*

Designed by Ron Bryant-Funnell

Cartoons in the Streetwise Evangelism
section are based on original artwork by
John Pickering from *One to One*
copyright Scripture Union

Cartoons on pages 10, 22, 24, 30, 31
and in the songs section
are by Sam Thompson

Printed in Great Britain for
KINGSWAY PUBLICATIONS LTD
1 St. Anne's Road, Eastbourne, E. Sussex BN21 3UN by
Stanley L. Hunt (Printers) Ltd, Rushden, Northants.

CONTENTS

PART TWO – SONGS, MUSIC

MAKE WAY! – SHINE, JESUS, SHINE
SONGS FOR THE STREETS (*in march order*)

MAKE WAY! – SHINE, JESUS, SHINE
SONGS OF WORSHIP & PRAYER (*in alphabetical order*)

PART THREE – SONGS, WORDS-ONLY

INTRODUCTION

In 1869 a Salvation Army reporter wrote in their paper *The East London Evangelist*:

'We have been much blessed in missioning the streets where the poorest reside. As we go singing down the street . . . doors fly open and windows shoot up, and soon we have eyes and ears on us from all sides. Every now and then we . . . pause, sing a verse or two, give a short address, publishing the glorious gospel . . . offer a few short earnest prayers; and then go on to another corner . . . .'

Praise, prayer and witness processions are by no means a new phenomenon! Outdoor events have had a special place in many phases of the church's history, and I believe that we are entering such a phase today.

Prayer, praise and witness processions can achieve many goals, from spiritual warfare to a joyful public witness to an expression of Christian unity. There is a dynamic involved which could be a key to a great spiritual breakthrough for the church, if only we could grasp it and use it. That dynamic is the strong, public declaration and celebration of truth. Satan's kingdom is built upon his lies and deceptions, but the truth that Jesus declared, when proclaimed with faith, is the very power that sets free those blinded by untruth. That power is greatly strengthened when spoken by throngs of people in unison.

Jesus said that the words He spoke were spirit and life. He has given us His words, and they can be spirit and life in our mouths, too. How desperately we need to rediscover that the truths we believe are not just concepts to hold in our minds. They are to be imbued by faith and the power of the Holy Spirit and so become divinely powered weapons in our spiritual warfare. It makes little difference whether they are spoken or sung. Every believer needs to learn how to use the 'sword of the Spirit'. We need to sing and celebrate with joyful authority the truth that Jesus Christ is the Son of God, born of a virgin, crucified, dead, buried, but raised to life. We need to proclaim that He is reigning at the right hand of the Father, soon to return to judge this world. We need to be a holy church, declaring with one voice these and other truths and living them out in the power of the Holy Spirit. As such we would be an unstoppable force.

I hope that the music and text of these processions will provide a useful tool for a prophetic church as it seeks to make the King of kings known to the ends of the earth in this generation.

MAKE WAY – WHY PRAISE PROCESSIONS?

With some notable exceptions, the streets of our villages, towns and cities have on the whole been left alone by the church, and the unpopular jobs of prayer and evangelism in the open air left to small, specialist groups with above-average boldness and below- average support from the rest of us. This state of affairs is nothing new as is clear when we look at the history of such movements as the early Methodists, or the Salvation Army (see page 18). It is, of course, easy to see how much more attractive it is to worship, pray or evangelise in the comfort and safety of a building, surrounded by a majority of sympathetic believers, rather than out in a public place surrounded by a majority of indifferent, curious or even antagonistic unbelievers.

However, a church that is too apathetic and afraid to risk the relatively minor inconveniences of such activities is never going to turn the tide of unbelief and evil in a locality, let alone reach the whole world for Christ – something which we are told is possible in one generation. For too long we have abdicated responsibility for the public, visible declaration of our faith, and abandoned the streets to political marches, political activists, cults, charity collectors, carnivals, and in many places to seedy street- life and an epidemic of violence. Political activity and carnivals can be entirely legitimate, but we believe it is time once again to invade the streets in the name of Christ!

VISIBILITY

Much has happened over the past twenty years in terms of church renewal, and many churches have sprung up, both within and without traditional denominations, full of new life and fresh expressions of God's presence among them. But this movement has been very much of an underground stream, and the general public has been largely unaware of what an attractive place 'church' can be. On more than one occasion, I have heard people who have seen Christians joyfully praising God comment: 'If I thought church was like that, I'd seriously think about going.'

It is time for the whole nation to recognise that the Christian church is a major force to be reckoned with, that it has a prophetic voice and a vital messsage to put across. Events like the City March in May 1987, which gathered well over 15,000 people, prove that we can probably raise as big a crowd as anyone else, and not only that, but a joyful, peaceful and responsible one too.

But there is much more to this whole vision than a show of strength. After all, the Lord said that it is 'not by might, nor by power, but by My Spirit' (Zech 4:6) that victories are won. The kind of strength in which we must stand as Christians, and the weapons God has given us – His word, prayer, the blood of Jesus, and our testimony to Him – are foolish in the world's view. Yet God has chosen the foolish things of this world to confound the so-called wise, and the weak things of this world to confound the strong (1 Cor 1:27, 28). Therefore we can march out with courage and gladness, praying and praising, declaring the truth of

God's word, and bearing testimony to Jesus who in the apparent weakness and foolishness of crucifixion won the decisive battle against the powers of sin and death and all their terrible consequences.

SPIRITUAL DYNAMICS

What are the particular 'dynamics' which make praise, prayer and witness processions effective?

Jesus described His words in this way: 'The words I have spoken to you are spirit and they are life' (Jn 6:63). Because the source of Jesus' words was in God himself, they were not only the truth in content, but were also endorsed by the accompanying activity of the Holy Spirit. As Jesus preached the good news of the kingdom of God, His words were authenticated by the signs and wonders that followed – He spoke and diseased bodies were healed, He spoke prophetically and shaped the future. His words were the breath of God, creating or destroying by the power of the Holy Spirit. The amazing fact is that God has given *us* His words, and His Spirit! All of us have the potential to speak and sing 'Spirit-energised words'.

DECLARATION – PROCLAMATION

For many Christians, the songs they sing are just pleasant anthems, pieces of cultural heritage, or poetic theology to be preserved. A new song is sometimes valued only for its novelty, or a hymn used merely as a programme-filler in a meeting. If this is our view, then that may be all they amount to in practice. My conviction is that properly understood and rightly used, our songs can become the spiritual equivalent of rockets exploding with joy in heaven and wreaking havoc in hell! How? Because our songs contain the most powerful energy in the universe – the word of God. In the deliberate act of singing praise, we lift the word of God up before heaven, before hell, and before men and women – and God does the rest.

I knew we should have sent the singers in first!

*'. . . our songs can become . . .
rockets exploding with joy
in heaven and wreaking havoc
in hell!'*

This is one of the strongest
dynamics of street marches,
simply because the word of
God is the Holy Spirit's
sword, and when His people
take His word by faith and
declare it in the power of the
Holy Spirit, God acts to
confirm and carry out His
word. We make a vital
connection between God's
word and every day reality
when we declare, for
example, that God is a just
God when passing a building
which symbolises something
to do with justice or injustice,
than when shut away in a
cosy church lounge.

We learn more about this dynamic from 2 Corinthians 10 which
describes the nature of spiritual strongholds. According to this passage,
the power of evil in the world is channelled through false ideas,
'arguments' and 'pretensions' that set themselves up against the
knowledge of God. Any Christian who has stood against Godless
ideologies knows that they are more than just ideas; they carry
enormous spiritual power and hold people in their grip. Jesus came
into this deceived world and declared: 'You will know the truth, and the
truth will set you free' (Jn 8:32). The truth needs to be declared with
authority, with love and humility, and with joy. When this happens the
power of God's word, which would otherwise remain hidden, is
released as the supremely potent force.

Once we have discovered that spiritual power is released when we
praise in this way, we must take care that we avoid a subtle danger. Our
focus can easily shift from the Lord Himself, and our delight in Him, to
our spiritual enemies. I believe that the effect of praise on the powers
of evil must be regarded as secondary, our primary aim being to praise
God for who He is. When King Jehoshaphat sent the singers out in front
of the army (2 Chron 20) they were appointed 'to sing to the Lord and
to praise Him for the splendour of his holiness . . . saying: "Give thanks
to the Lord, for His love endures for ever." ' Theirs was a joyful song,
pre-occupied with God. As they praised Him, He dealt with their
enemies.

CONFESSION AND INTERCESSION

It is the privilege and responsibility of the church to stand before God on behalf of the nation in which it is placed, and to pray. Daniel is a prime example of someone who not only prayed for his own nation, as well as the one in which he was an exile, but also confessed their sins before the Lord even though he himself was a righteous man. Make Way events provide a framework in which this can be done. They can take confession and intercession to places where the need for God's mercy and forgiveness is most apparent, and where the consequences of sin are hurting people the most.

It is tremendously important that we as the church confess our part in failing to speak out and act in our society as we should have done. Confession militates against the appearance of condemning others in a self-righteous way. Confession should progress into intercession as we seek to catch what is on God's heart for the nation, city, town or village, and set our eyes on the future.

WARNING

A look at Ezekiel 33 suggests that those who claim to speak from God have a grave responsibility to warn of the consequences of rebellion against God's laws of love, as well as to proclaim the good news. Again, we have no right to be judgemental or superior, rather we should speak out of humility and compassion.

THE WITNESS OF OUR PRESENCE

It is not only the words we speak that witness to Christ, but also our very presence, and what people read in our faces, behaviour and attitudes. In addition, we should not underestimate the impact made on people as they sense God's presence with us as we pass. Let us not forget that genuine joy, love, hope and friendliness are in short supply on the streets, and for some people merely to sense the atmosphere is enough to convince them that God is real and among us. Of course, we must not think that we can switch on the Holy Spirit at our convenience. Rather, Scripture shows that it is often in worship that God chooses to manifest His presence in a special way. Once again, our part is to praise, pray and witness. He does the rest. Our joyful and colourful presence on the streets also serves to break the caricatures of Christianity that exist in people's minds, and reintroduce them to the church as a joyful company of people, full of life and colour, with a message relevant to today's world. (A march is an excellent springboard for all kinds of ancillary evangelistic activities, and some ideas are presented later in this handbook.)

It is important to keep firmly in mind that we witness not only to people, but also to spiritual powers that influence our society. On the positive side, we worship and proclaim with 'the whole company of heaven', who are constantly singing God's praise and declaring His attributes, but we also confront the powers of darkness with the truth of Christ. Paul describes his own part in this calling of the church in Ephesians 3:9-10 – 'to make all men see what is the plan of the mystery hidden for ages in God who created all things; that through the church the manifold wisdom of God might now be made known to the principalities and powers in the heavenly places' (Revised Standard Version).

MARCHING IN UNITY

The phenomenon of churches from different traditions, denominations and locations marching, witnessing and praying together is a very dynamic one. 'When brothers live together in unity . . . there the Lord bestows his blessing,' wrote the Psalmist (Ps 133:1,3). Just how much the work of God's Spirit is restricted by disunity hardly bears thinking about, and sheer ignorance of the life of other Christian groups leaves a vacuum of friendship, love and co-operation. However, when we can gather together under the banner of Christ and celebrate the basic truths of the gospel, who knows what fresh moves of the Spirit there might be, and what sharing of resources and opportunities to love and serve might occur?

There is also the 'dynamic' of agreeing together over an issue as the Spirit moves a great crowd to pray together. Let's push the limits of what can be achieved by such praying until we discover in practice that there are no limits.

A BAPTISM OF BOLDNESS

If there was no other benefit to praise, prayer and witness processions than an increasing boldness on behalf of the participants, then I feel the whole event would still be very worth while. I frequently wonder at the difference in atmosphere among a group of marchers before and after a march. Before, they are often reserved and restrained, nervous if they have never done anything like it before, possibly feeling foolish holding a banner, or fearful of having to pass out leaflets to strangers (or friends!). After . . . every march that I have personally seen has ended with a great sense of excitement, with many individuals set free in their spirits through the act of public confession of their faith. Many will have witnessed to their belief 'en masse' or one to one for the first time, and exchanged their shyness for boldness. Make sure that this boldness and enthusiasm is harnessed immediately (see Chapter 7, the section 'Beware the Fizzle Factor'!, and further ideas for street events).

Can we measure the concrete effects of such declarations, or are we merely fooling ourselves about their power and effects? It is hard to quantify the results of such activities immediately. Essentially they are an act of faith, but if that faith is genuine then it will bear fruit in time. There have been exciting reports of people being converted during marches, and reports of an unusual openness to the Gospel on the streets and in town centres immediately following or during a march. I believe that this will increase.

But this is not primarily the aim. Where serious prayer, praise and witness marches take place as part of an on-going programme (including practical action for justice and for people in need), we aim for breakthrough in some of the following areas:

(1) A new openness to the Gospel; fresh opportunities to witness resulting in more conversions.
(2) The exposure of corruption and the breaking of evil and unjust practices in areas of society.
(3) Positive change in the policies, practices or laws of governing bodies.
(4) The establishment of more God-fearing people in places of responsibility.
(5) Breakthroughs in establishing new churches in the areas where the march takes place.
(6) Greater unity and co-operation between churches and Christian organisations.
(7) A greater awareness of the local church's message and character by the surrounding community.
(8) A new spirit of boldness among participating Christians.

NB: We may also encounter increasing opposition from some quarters.

The above are all potential areas for breakthrough. I do not wish to set any limits on what is possible, for our God specialises in impossibilities. However, praise and witness marches involve spiritual warfare, and there is a danger that people will adopt unrealistic aims in dealing with the powers of darkness, especially if seen as a one-off event. I am more and more convinced that the message of Exodus 23:30 is appropriate in this respect: 'Little by little I will drive them out before you, until you have increased enough to take possession of the land.' If we really want to break the grip of the powers of darkness in a locality, it may need to happen little by little as the church grows in authority, love and holiness.

Furthermore, it is unhelpful if unbelievers are subjected to singing, praising and shouting Christians who they know very well never do anything practical to bring righteousness and justice into the locality. Such events ideally go alongside involvement in the needs of the whole person so that we are not seen simply as people full of hot air, without real substance in our lives.

A FLEXIBLE RESOURCE

Many different ingredients go to make up a praise, prayer and witness procession. Although the *Make Way* album is a fixed sequence, in practice the strength and emphasis of the various ingredients can be altered to fine-tune the content as required in each situation. Prayer of one kind or another may particularly need to be organised, or perhaps strong praise, witness, or an expression of unity. Corporate prayers, shouts, etc, can be added as appropriate, additional prayer scripts relating to the march route appended in a programme, and the visual appearance of the march adapted as required. For example, a march for the sole purpose of prayer may not necessarily need to go through a busy shopping street, or give as much attention to visual effects (though banners carried with faith can be as much a declaration to the spiritual powers as words spoken or sung).

'NOW IS THE TIME FOR US TO MARCH UPON THE LAND'

It seems to me and many others that now is a crucial time to invade the streets with the above aims in view. We often forget that we are among a privileged minority of nations that are freely able to undertake this kind of public demonstration. Even in Britain tighter restrictions have recently been placed on marches, and there are many powerful groups who would like to see Christians effectively banned from streets altogether. We need to make the most of the present opportunity and establish a strong presence among all the other groups who regularly demonstrate, celebrate or 'evangelise' on the streets. However, of far greater importance than 'staking our claim' in this area of the nation's life is the ever-present urgency of taking the good news of the kingdom of God to the people, through prayer, through praise and proclamation, and through witness and practical action.

To me, what is most exciting is not just filling the streets with processions, but what the whole initiative might lead to once Christians have gained a new confidence and boldness in the public arena of their community, and indeed their nation.

NOTHING NEW – SOME GLIMPSES OF CHURCH HISTORY

'There is nothing new under the sun,' as the world-weary writer of Ecclesiastes commented (Eccles 1:9). Worship in the open air is no exception – it has all been done before. The interesting thing is that where it has been done before it has very often been connected with religious revival.

The earliest record in England of Christian songs being used outdoors is in AD 675. Alfred the Great's handbook records how Aldhelm, the Abbott of Malmesbury, decided that if the people wouldn't come to the message then the message would have to come to them. Aldhelm had studied music in Rome. When he returned to Wessex, the people obviously liked his music, but had taken to leaving church before the sermon started. As they came out, Aldhelm would be there singing the popular songs of the day, progressing to songs with a Christian message and slipping in a crafty preach when he'd gathered a crowd!

The medieval monks were the evangelists of their day and many of them didn't hesitate to use new forms of music in their missions. St Bernard of Clairvaux (1090-1153) founded his own monastery and was a great church reformer, but he also moved among the common people, preaching, singing and performing signs and wonders in the open fields and town squares. Maybe this timeless hymn was first made popular among peasants in the French counryside:

> Jesus, Thou joy of loving hearts,
> Thou fount of life, Thou light of men,
> From the best bliss which earth imparts,
> We turn unfilled to Thee again.

John Huss, leader of a revival movement in the fifteenth century, composed folk hymns in his native Czech for his followers to sing as they met in market-places, fields and meadows.

The Catholic and Orthodox churches still continue the tradition of processions in many places today, particularly those associated with pilgrimage. The banners you often see hanging inside Anglican churches were not intended for that purpose, but for taking out around the parish. Whit Sunday has always been a time for Christian processions, especially in the Midlands and the North of England.

The idea of taking the Gospel out to where the people are hasn't always met with enthusiasm, even among church leaders. John Wesley was shocked when it was first suggested that he might preach to the miners of Bristol out in the fields:

'31st March 1739 . . . I thought the saving of souls almost a sin if it had not been done in a church.'

He pondered the problem and reflected that Jesus did most of his preaching outdoors:

'2nd April 1739 . . . At 4 in the afternoon I submitted to be more vile and proclaimed in the highways the glad tidings of salvation.'

It is interesting to speculate what might have happened to the history of the church, and even of our nation, if Wesley had not 'submitted to be more vile.'

The Salvation Army took their brass bands onto the streets in the late nineteenth century. They were not always very popular. The *Worthing Gazette* of 1883 described them as 'excitable young men and hysterical young women who mistake a quasi-religious revelry for Godliness.' At about the same time *Punch* magazine wrote about 'Bootheration':

A procession is a nuisance at any time, and should only be permitted on rare and exceptional occasions. As to the noisy Religious Services which disturb the peace and quiet of neighbourhoods on the Day of Rest, they should all be confined within the four walls of their own Tabernacle, Camp, Church or Conventicle, whatever it may be, and those walls should be, by Act of Parliament, of sufficient thickness to prevent the escape of noise.

In one twelve-month period 669 Salvationists were assaulted, 56 Army buildings were stoned and damaged, and 86 members of the Army were jailed by magistrates. But the Army grew. In under ten years it had expanded twenty times over. The Army became respected and revered, perhaps because it backed up its noise with a great deal of social concern and action.

One of the Salvation Army's greatest processions was in 1885. It marched to the Houses of Parliament with a petition two miles long, bearing 343,000 signatures demanding that the trade in child prostitution (which was rampant at the time) be stopped and the age of consent raised from thirteen to sixteen years old. They succeeded and lives were changed. Drunkards sobered up and started to care for their

families; prostitutes gave up their ways and turned to respectable employment. Salvation had turned their lives around. A converted coal-cart driver summed it up. 'Well,' he said, 'no smoking, no drinking, no swearing, and the 'orses know the difference.' The world began to notice the difference too.

General Booth didn't see why the devil should have all the good tunes and the Army borrowed them shamelessly. This early Salvationist song goes to the tune of 'The Campbells are coming'.

The Army is coming – amen, amen!
To conquer this city for Jesus – amen!
We'll shout 'Hallelujah!' and praise His dear name,
Who redeemed us to God through the blood of the Lamb.
The sound of its footsteps is rolling along;
The kingdom of Satan, triumphant so long,
Is shaking and tott'ring and downward shall fall,
For Jesus the Saviour shall reign over all.

When the Spirit was poured out upon Wales in 1904, society could not escape its impact. For a time the courts had no new cases to try and the taverns emptied. A report read:

'Perhaps the most prominent feature is the lessening of drunkenness, for the night marches [converts on their way home from meetings] of praying and singing converts seem to have induced a considerable number of converts to abandon their evil ways.' Another commentator wrote:

'The revival of 1904 united denominations as one body, filled the chapels nightly, renewed family ties, changed life in mines and factories, often crowded streets with huge processions, abated social vices and diminished crime.

AND NOW – in recent years God has been moving inside the churches like an underground stream, bringing new growth and vitality. This is beginning to burst out. The church is becoming visible again. It has a voice which needs to be heard. The time has come to take to the streets again!

SO YOU WANT TO GO PRAISE MARCHING?

WHEN

Obviously, Saturdays are the most popular time, but some groups have effectively used Make Way on Sundays. One church regularly marches to morning service from homes in its area, covering a different route each time. Why not use the Sunday morning service as a 'warm-up' and process out afterwards. Fine summer Sunday afternoons draw a lot of people to the park and many parks have bandstands just waiting to be used (but investigate the bye-laws first – see the section on permission). Don't assume that open-air witness equals summer. Some very effective praise marches have been done in the winter, especially around Christmas time. Most Christmas carols have been around for a long while. Look out for Make Way – Christmas style!

WHERE

Shopping streets. These are excellent for maximum visibility, as long as they are not too busy. Bringing the town centre to a halt may cause a stir, but it won't make you very popular if you do it too often!

Pedestrian precincts. These are much easier, with no traffic control and noise to worry about. Some shopping precincts are privately owned so you need to get permission if you are going to be there for any length of time.

Housing estates. Only if there is good visibility from the flats and plenty of space to march. Choose a time when people are likely to be out and about (eg, not Cup Final afternoon). You could send a squad leafleting, either beforehand to warn that you're coming, or while the march is going on if you can spare enough people.

It is very effective to march between a series of suitable sites, such as the quadrangles formed by a group of high-rise blocks, stopping for a brief presentation in word, drama, etc before moving on. Don't outstay your welcome however, there may be some people on night shift who are trying to sleep! You could invite people down to watch and offer fruit punch or balloons for the kids, say who you are and leave a leaflet, including an address or helpline, inviting people to meetings. Note any 'warm' contacts for follow-up.

Around the perimeter of your patch. The good old Anglican tradition has a word for this! Rogationtide (five weeks after Easter) when you beat the bounds of the parish. The custom dates from medieval times when the whole village marched round to identify its boundary and 'beat back the devil'. Why not do it in song?

In Birmingham they have successfully organised an interdenominational march around the ring road, encircling the city with praise. They divided the marchers up into groups starting at ten different points and covering just over two miles each. Twenty-three miles in all – that's some parish boundary!

And also. The red light district, the village green, the sea front, council offices, tourist attractions, parks, slums, the centres of government and commerce. Wherever you need to declare the Lordship and love of Jesus – that's the place to do it.

Check there are no obstructions to your planned route.

As an act of witness the procession should be in a place where it is visible, audible, and will receive a high profile. This is not so essential if your primary aim is prayer. You should not cause any obstruction to the public right of way. Plan the route carefully, look out for obstructions which could slow the procession down or break up continuity. Will wheel-chairs and push-chairs make it? How long will it take? Processions tend to move more slowly than normal walking pace. Walk your route, time it, and generally check it out.

HOW

The method you use will depend on the size of your group, your resources, and your particular aims. Make Way has been done by anything between a couple of dozen and 15,000 people.

Companies. A group of anything up to 200 people can march in one unit, kept tightly together. Musicians can be in the centre, depending on the volume and clarity of the music. The more spread out the march, the further the music has to carry. Marching three abreast, for instance, creates a procession twice as long as six abreast.

Large groups may be best with a brass band in the centre or towards the rear of the procession so that the sound can carry. You could involve the local Salvation Army band, who would be happy to give you advice – they have 100 years of experience, after all!

Crowds. Larger groups than the above need to be divided up into clearly defined units with musicians in the centre of each. The people on the fringes of each unit may have difficulty knowing who to sing along with, so either leave a non-singing 'buffer' group between each bunch, or better still put a group of prayers between each musical group. Their job would primarily be to intercede as the march is progressing (they'd better keep their eyes open, though!).

Another method is to use a series of vehicles, each with a synchronised sound system playing the Make Way tape for people to sing along to. It is necessary to use high quality reel-to-reel tape machines to get accurate timing. The tapes start together in synchronisation and then the vehicles move off at intervals. In order to cope with a march longer than twenty minutes, record the music several times over without gaps. The beauty of this method is that the whole march sings simultaneously, though the technical risks are

higher. If all goes well, by the end of the march all the tape machines are still synchronised to within a fraction of a second.

An exciting idea which may be worth exploring is using a radio link-up. Marchers carrying their own portable radios could tune in to a live broadcast. This depends on broadcasting regulations and policies in force at the time. Contact your local radio station and encourage them to give you some live coverage.

Do not stand too close to lorry.

Carnival style. Use an amplified band on the back of a lorry with marchers in front and behind. But beware! One group found the people immediately behind the lorry were overcome with exhaust fumes! Avoid hiring a smoky vehicle in the first place.

Two open-sided curtain lorries backed onto each other can provide a large effective stage area for starting and finishing points as well as providing transport on the march, with the added advantage of a roof

The police sometimes like vehicles in processions to move at traffic speed, so you may have to have the singers, similarly amplified, on other lorries. (Or else have them going for a praise jog!) If the police require you to move too fast, the music will not be effective.

You could march as part of your town's annual carnival, or make your own with a series of floats on a Christian theme.

You could use other modes of transport. One church used a tractor at the head of the procession, another had the vicar on horseback, one thoughtfully included a minibus for the old folk.

Converging. Why not have smaller processions from all over town converging on one central point where they can all join together in a combined act of worship? What more vivid expression of the churches' diversity and yet unity?

And then there's the Mega-March. Once you get into the thousands of people bracket (and we are beginning to see more and more of this), the planning starts to get rather complex. On a march of this size you may need crowd barriers, staging at each end of the route, extra public loos, and an awful lot of stewarding. Not something to be undertaken lightly, so make sure you hear from God before you embark on it.

NB: You don't have to have musicians. A proven alternative is to use *Make Way* cassettes and sing with them. These could be with car-mounted speakers (one small group just used a series of powerful car stereos with the car windows open), battery public address, or even a good quality stereo cassette player. To ensure a strong beat to keep everyone in time, a live bass drum may need to be added, the drummer keeping close enough to the sound source to keep in time himself.

You don't even have to march. Use *Make Way* on the move wherever you can, but where a procession isn't possible, use *Make Way* as a static open-air celebration in a suitable part of the town, sea front or park. Look out for local events which you could take part in, such as the village May fayre or the county show.

GETTING TO WORK

PARTICIPATION

Involve other churches in your area if you can. As far as possible *Make Way* should be an interdenominational event, a public witness to the unity of the body of Christ. Many reports of marches stressed how good it was to be working with other Christians in this way.

> 'Some important ongoing friendships have been established among the leaders who planned it, and people have been given a sense of corporateness, and their vision has been enlarged and challenged.
>
> It was good to feel a major presence instead of being a minority group.
>
> The thrilling thing about the whole event was the way the whole body of Christ came together . . . . We expected between 300 and 500, 700-800 came.
>
> It was fantastic . . . . To watch them turn the corner and see the banners and people praising the Lord was the most wonderful thing I'd ever seen.'
>
> *Salvation Army lady at North Staffordshire march.*

An interchurch march may take more effort, but it will be worth while. It will involve:

Planning – More organisation and committees will be needed. It may be good to organise rehearsals together, or a joint celebration where different groups can get used to worshipping and praying with each other.

Personal invitation – This is better than sending a piece of paper. Beware! Church secretaries' waste-paper bins are full of unsolicited bumph, so find out the person most likely to be interested. If necessary, be prepared to go along and explain the concept. Share the vision, let other people catch your enthusiasm.

Publicity – give full information and keep all concerned updated about the march.

> A twenty-minute training video in which Graham Kendrick explains the concept of *Make Way*, with examples taken from actual marches, is available for sale or hire (see Appendix). People can grasp the idea much more easily by seeing it in practice.

PLANNING THE PROGRAMME

Make Way processions are designed for the streets, using a sequence of songs, shouts and prayers. Of course, additional material may be used in specific circumstances. The important thing is to make sure everyone is clear about which songs to sing and in which order they should be sung.

Music books are available with the basic piano part and guitar chords. *Make Way! – A Carnival of Praise* songs are in the *Graham Kendrick Songbook* Volume 2. Simple band arrangements are integral to the 'Shine, Jesus, Shine' music book. Make sure your musicians have enough copies.

TEACH THE SONGS

— During, before or after regular meetings, at house groups, etc.
— By encouraging people to listen to the tape individually – in the car, doing the housework, etc.
— In special rehearsals.
— By rehearsing a core choir as well as the congregation. But don't let the others think they can come totally unprepared.

Encourage people to learn the words – it isn't quite so liberating to have your nose in a book. But in any case, make sure sufficient Marchers' booklets are available on the day. Ideally, participants should obtain their Marchers' Handbook some weeks in advance.

The songs should be familiar enough to people that they can go out worshipping and not be struggling to get them right.

TRAIN THE BAND

Rhythm. A variety of different instruments can be used, but it is most important to have a clear rhythm. The big bass drum, carried by a strong person with a good sense of rhythm, is by far the best way of setting the beat. Add to that a snare drum or a side drum, suitably

harnessed, and you have a versatile unit. There is quite an art to keeping the right tempo and changing it between songs. If the drummer is unsure, a prepared cassette in a personal hi-fi, or a portable electronic metronome (common among drummers) could cue him in to the right beat. We have noted the beats per minute in the music book. Even during the gaps between songs, when prayers or corporate readings are taking place, let the drums continue. They announce the march from far off and maintain the sense of occasion. It has been observed that if a march lapses into silence, its energy and effectiveness quickly dissipates.

Guitars are fine, but their sound does not travel very well. Treat them as part of the rhythm section and keep them close to the drum. One 'first' guitarist could be amplified.

No independent tambourines! This is not to say that a well-rehearsed single percussionist or even a timbrel group cannot add to the music, but a rogue tambourinist can play havoc with the rhythm and cause a musical free-for-all – not a good witness!

Shine, Je - sus, shine,

Melody. The best way of carrying the melody is with brass instruments or wind instruments such as the flute and clarinet. Try and get a full brass band for larger gatherings. Brass parts are available (see Appendix).

The shout leader. Obviously someone with a loud voice, but also with a good sense of rhythm. Place him near the drum and give him some PA. He could be combined with either of the two following roles.

The song leader. He must give a clear, confident lead and set the tone of the event. He must be able to lead the band, cue the songs, correct errors quickly, and keep the momentum of the worship. He requires a microphone – held by someone else or headphone mounted if he is also playing an instrument.

The prayer leader. People usually need to be given a strong lead, instructions, prayer points, and general encouragement to achieve maximum participation. Look for someone gifted to get people responding. Preachers and evangelists are often good in this role, musicians not so often! If there are pauses in the programme where people are unsure of what is going on, it will quickly degenerate into chit-chat. So be prepared to step in quickly.

One of these people should be prepared to give a bright and brief explanation to the public of who you are and why you are marching. Please avoid Christian jargon or you will make people feel more alienated. Be friendly, not aggressive or judgemental. You're sharing good news, not bad!

Rehearsal. Make sure the musicians are personally invited, competent, well-rehearsed and used to playing together and also on the move. Practise walking and playing in formation as soon as possible. Improvise a device for holding your music, if you need to (you could mount it on the back of the person in front). Cover it in a plastic folder to stop the ravages of wind and rain, and work out how to change sheets for a continuous series of songs.

If the band is on a lorry with a generator, you have the freedom to use more regular 'indoor' instruments such as a drum kit, electric piano, or bass. Rehearse in a similar space to the lorry flat-bed. Do you all fit on?

NB: Stopping and starting a lorry can be a violent operation. People and equipment need to be secure so that if the driver suddenly applies air-brakes the band does not collapse in a cacophonous heap! Going round corners can be interesting too. When travelling at traffic speed in a vehicle not designed for passenger use, certain safety regulations must be observed. Do not take risks!

Despite technical demands, encourage the musicians to worship. Try to make the standard of music as good as possible, but remember, as one group reported, 'It wasn't perfection or professionalism which made the impact, but enthusiasm.'

CHILDREN

Children are a major part of the church's life and witness, and should be encouraged to get fully involved at their various age-levels and abilities. They can learn simple dances, or hold balloons, placards or small banners. They can wave 'swizzle sticks', dress as clowns, and play ocarinas or recorders. However, do not underestimate their ability to contribute to the spiritual impact of the march through praise and prayer. As already mentioned, Psalm 8 reminds us of the powerful effect of children's praises: 'From the lips of children and infants You have ordained praise because of Your enemies, to silence the foe and the avenger' (Ps 8:2). Children's workshops and Sunday School activities can be used to prepare them for full participation.

OCARINAS

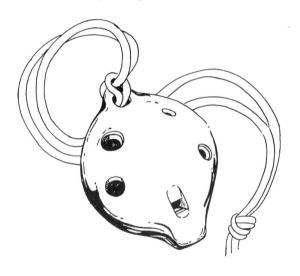

Ocarinas are small, four-hole flutes that are easy to play and can be worn around the neck as pendants. They are fun for all ages and have a beautiful sound when played solo or in groups.

Ocarinas are easier to play than recorders. Simple charts show which holes to cover for each note and non-musicians can teach themselves to play successfully without having to read music, making them a good instrument for the family. Older children can master a few simple tunes in a forty-minute workshop.

The Alto ocarina in D is ideal for many of the *Make Way* songs and makes an exciting addition to any music group. For further information please write to The Ocarina Workshop, or for details of the *Make Way* ocarina package write to Make Way Music, see addresses in Appendix. The Ocarina Workshop may be able to run a workshop as part of your march preparation.

Ocarinas – notes for leaders.

The best way to play for processions is from memory. Learning a few particular songs well on the ocarina is better than attempting several songs badly. If you have to carry music, plan very carefully how to do it.

Although most people can learn to play successfully, some skill is needed and practice is essential for individuals and groups. Fortunately, unlike the recorder, the sound can be attractive even when some are playing wrong notes!

The effects of wind and cold can be hazardous to all blowing instruments. Ocarinas go out of tune (flat) on cold days and are difficult to play in strong winds.

Plan how you can make best use of the ocarinas and players. Their sound will appeal to passers-by and their use can involve people instrumentally who would not normally be part of the band. Large numbers of players can be very effective if well organised – this is obviously ideal for 'Make Way' marches.

PUBLIC ADDRESS

You will need a portable amplifier capable of high-level output without distortion. Test for quality – some horn-type systems are OK for speech but terrible for music. It could be carried on a rucksack frame, in a shopping trolley, push-chair, pram or wheel-chair (but try not to let it look too silly). If using wheels, make sure the device can negotiate kerbs. Or be innovative – one sound system carried on the city march looked amazingly reminiscent of the Ark of the Covenant!.

I don't think that's quite what they meant!

You will need two loudspeakers, to point forwards and backwards. They need to be carried above the heads of the crowd, so mount them on some sort of pole.

★★★

PROCESSION ORDER

NEXT GROUP

PRAYERS

SINGERS

MUSICIANS
VIOLIN
FLUTES
GUITARS

LOUD
SPEAKER

SONG
LEADER

SHOU...
LEAD...

★★★

Use a good quality microphone, and make sure you have a windshield. A quality megaphone is fine for spoken words but not ideal for music. But it is good for a stand- by.

Are your batteries fully charged? Do you have enough to last the length of the march? Do you have spares?

If singing with a tape, carry a spare in case of failure. Run it simultaneously on a 'Walkman' player or something similar, so that if needed it will be roughly at the same point in the sequence as the first one.

A generator can be used on a lorry or at a static site. Be warned! They are noisy. Be careful! One keen musician borrowed a builder's generator and blew up his amplifier! An inverter can be used to provide 240 volts AC from a 12-volt car battery. Warning! It will drain the battery quickly. Lamp-posts often contain 13-amp sockets. Ask the council – they may let you plug in.

Above all, make sure you use well-maintained equipment competently put together, otherwise one loose wire and – silence. Try it out beforehand. Bring your sound expert with you on the march.

NB: Don't make more noise than is actually required, especially on a static site – it will not endear you to the neighbourhood.

For advice on the sort of equipment you need, go to a PA specialist. The names of some Christian firms are listed in the *UK Christian Handbook* (Marc Europe: Bromley, 1986). You may also be able to hire equipment if necessary.

LOUD SPEAKER

DRUM

MUSICIANS BRASS

SINGERS

DANCERS

LEAD BANNER

GOD IS GOOD

POLICE AND PUBLIC HIGHWAYS

It is our right to hold an act of public worship in the open air, but our duty not to cause an obstruction or disturbance of the peace. It is the job of the police to decide whether this is likely. The 1986 Public Order Act has tightened up on the laws regarding marches, and the police now have more power to impose conditions on a procession, but only if they have reason to believe you may cause a public disorder. There is provision in the law for any conditions set down to be challenged, so make sure you clarify matters at an early stage.

In any case, you must write at least one week beforehand (preferably sooner) to the Chief Superintendent (Operations) at your local police station telling him what you want to do. Include the following information:

— Name, address and phone number of march organiser.
— Date of march, starting and finishing times.
— Assembly point, route and finishing point.
— Approximate number of people.
— Any vehicles involved – how many, what sort.
— Whether a meeting is to be held before or after the procession.
— What parking arrangements have been made.
— Name of person in charge on the day of the march and where to find him.
— Whether any organisation is likely to demonstrate in opposition!

You need not ask for a police escort – they will decide if it is necessary, and also the amount of police presence required. The police may be somewhat bemused by what you are doing, but they are usually very helpful. At one major city march, the police inspector told the organiser, 'This is your day, go and enjoy it'.

- Demonstrate that you are a well-organised and responsible group.
- Be courteous – the police have lots of other problems to think about.
- Be firm and persistent – don't take no for an answer, but be flexible and respect their advice.
- When discussing the route along roads, always try to insist on taking the whole of a carriageway in one direction. It's better than only taking half and then having vehicles scraping up the outside.
- Pray for the police on the march and give them plenty of thanks afterwards.

PERMISSION

Parks. Parks are usually run by local authorities and most have by-laws restricting the playing of music, particularly amplified, but they may well allow you if you ask. Chat to the park-keeper if you can, otherwise write to the council. Beware! it can take endless committees, so apply well in advance. If you are a small enough group to be flexible, book several options – the weather may not always be kind.

Housing estates. These are the property of the local authority and technically their permission should be sought, but your request could easily sink in a sea of red tape, so use your discretion.

Shopping precincts. These are often privately owned. They sometimes have a manager on the premises, bu may be run by an absentee property company. Either way, make sure they give you written permission. Managements are often amenable, especially if they think that more people coming into the centre equals more profit!

The way in which requests are put across is often the deciding factor. Present the event as something attractive, positive and as an expression of the local community. Stress that you are a local community group and that you want to do something positive in the town. It helps if you can truthfully say that you represent so many thousand local people, ie the total membership of the participating churches. Personal contact is always an advantage, so try to find out the name of the correct person to get in touch with and deal with them direct.

After the march, don't forget to say thank you, and clear up any mess you have made. This is not only a good witness, it may help you get permission next time.

PRESS RELEASES

You may wish to spread the message even further than the limits of your PA system by getting a write-up in your local paper or a report on local radio. Send a press release at least one week in advance of the event to *all* local papers and radio stations. Explain clearly who, what, where, when and why. Do not use theological jargon. You may know what 'claiming ground' and 'breaking Satan's stronghold' mean, but your local paper may put it as 'church take-over bid' and 'religious group say town is demon- possessed'!

If they do not send a reporter, you can send your report and even black-and-white photos after the event, but act quickly. Most local papers need their copy in on the Tuesday immediately after the event for publication on Thursday or Friday.

See *Your Church and the Media*, a workbook by Nigel Sharp (address in Appendix).

PRAYER

This is the most important preparation of all. Without it, all the rest is worthless. Musicians, planners, dancers, banner-makers – only if all our practical activity is steeped in prayer will the end result carry the Spirit's life with it.

Before the day

— Hold special prayer meetings if you can.
— Make it part of your church's regular prayer life.
— Issue pointers to prayer with your in-house publicity material.
— Send everyone on a 'prayer-stroll' – pray round the route beforehand informally in twos and threes.

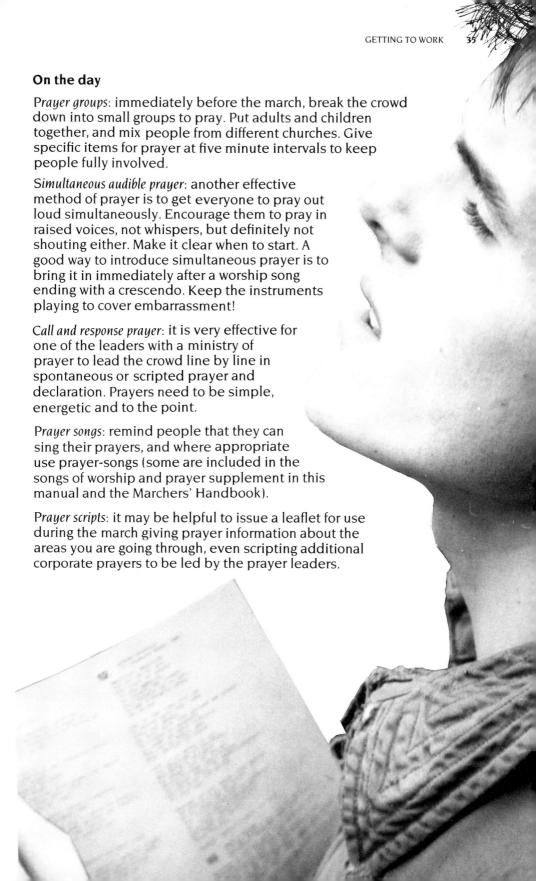

On the day

Prayer groups: immediately before the march, break the crowd down into small groups to pray. Put adults and children together, and mix people from different churches. Give specific items for prayer at five minute intervals to keep people fully involved.

Simultaneous audible prayer: another effective method of prayer is to get everyone to pray out loud simultaneously. Encourage them to pray in raised voices, not whispers, but definitely not shouting either. Make it clear when to start. A good way to introduce simultaneous prayer is to bring it in immediately after a worship song ending with a crescendo. Keep the instruments playing to cover embarrassment!

Call and response prayer: it is very effective for one of the leaders with a ministry of prayer to lead the crowd line by line in spontaneous or scripted prayer and declaration. Prayers need to be simple, energetic and to the point.

Prayer songs: remind people that they can sing their prayers, and where appropriate use prayer-songs (some are included in the songs of worship and prayer supplement in this manual and the Marchers' Handbook).

Prayer scripts: it may be helpful to issue a leaflet for use during the march giving prayer information about the areas you are going through, even scripting additional corporate prayers to be led by the prayer leaders.

Prayer sections: sections of the march can be made up of groups of people with a ministry of prayer, possibly with no obligation to sing. They need to be well motivated and able to sustain a long period of prayer, preferably out loud. They can also serve as a non- singing 'buffer' zone between groups singing at different rates. NB: be sure to instruct people clearly in advance about how and what to pray as they march.

Prayer should continue after the event. Who knows what long-term repercussions will result when Christians step out in faith declaring Jesus as Lord? Pray it through!

MARCH ADMINISTRATION – SOME BASIC GUIDELINES

The amount of administration necessary obviously depends on the size of march that you are planning. The bigger the march, the more people you will need to organise it. However, keep your central organising group small, but make sure that all the areas you will cover during the event are represented. For larger events you will need to identify heads of responsibility and give them full freedom, but they must come back to your group with their proposals worked out in writing. Below is a list of different areas of responsibility. The number of people who take on these responsibilities again depends on the size of event you are running, so if you have a march of only 100 you will probably only need one or two people organising the whole event.

Event administrator. This person is in overall charge of everyone else. He liaises with the police, and stays with the senior police officer on the day of the event. On a large march it is useful to set up an office where he can be based and where communications can be run from. Don't position this office in a noisy place, such as near your main PA! This person also deals with public relations, and should know at all times who is in charge of what so that any problems that arise can be delegated very quickly. He must also thoroughly brief any leaders who will take part in the event but are not part of the planning group. However, remember that any instructions given on the day to leaders or the whole assembly must be simple and must be repeated.

Chief steward. On a large march this person should not have to do any stewarding, but co-ordinate all the other stewards. The chief steward should start the march and move with the front of the march. His team should be large enough to ensure at least one steward to every fifty marchers. These stewards are assigned to a particular group and should be clearly identifiable by wearing armbands or sashes. If you have stewards from a particular group, then if possible let them steward that group. Their main job is to stay with their group, making sure that they keep up the pace. If you split up at all you may end up with a bus in between groups!

March marshalls. These people should be placed at strategic points along the route. They can be used as markers for starting points on prayer-scripts, but they should also keep an eye on how the march is going. As stewards of each group pass by them, any problems can be relayed. On a large march certain marshalls could be in radio contact with each other and the main base. If this is not possible, then any problems could be relayed through the police, who should be with the whole march, and the main administrator.

Site manager. If you are starting or finishing with a rally, you will need someone who is responsible for your rally site, its equipment and lay-out. He can also be in charge of any staging, but for a very large march you may also need a stage manager. The site manager must also be responsible for the cleaning-up of the site once everyone has departed. (Make an announcement asking everyone to pick up rubbish as they leave.)

Press officer. You may need to have someone in charge of media relations to deal with the press and other media. Make sure that you tell the media what is happening or they might pick up misinformation from an unreliable source or impose their own preconceived ideas about the event. This person can also be in charge of informing other groups of what is happening. He should be available at the event at some obvious place, such as by the stage, to answer all media questions and explain what is going on.

Bit and pieces. Don't forget to inform people like the St John Ambulance if you are having a big march.

Keep the organisation of the event as simple as possible, and establish clear lines of communication. One of the first things that you should do as a group is to decide upon your route and then walk it, timing how long this takes and noting any obstructions like level-crossing gates, subways and bollards.

Don't forget to inform the police as early as possible, and also contact your local authority. When meeting any of these groups make sure you are fully prepared and know exactly what you want. Don't go alone as usually they will only meet you if you have someone with you. Make very clear who you are – most other marches are negative demonstrations, so they may view you in this way to begin with. If you are organising staging, or have a large public gathering, then you will also need to contact the borough engineers and surveyors.

At a large event you will need a full PA system. Get in professionals for this job and don't leave it to someone who may run a small PA in their church. If the people on the march cannot hear your instructions on the day they could all end up going the wrong way!

On the day of a large march make sure you stagger the arrivals so that you don't have pandemonium right at the start. However, don't assume that people will arrive when you told them to – they will usually turn up too early. Groups that are waiting for others to arrive can spend the time praying. Be careful when walking through traffic that all children are kept under control. Also, be diplomatic when walking through shopping areas and across bus routes. Do *not* stop to pray while on your march unless you are quite a small group. Get people praying while they walk.

Finally, expect that the event will not go to plan. Make sure that everyone knows who to relate to, and for what problem, when the unexpected arises.

MAKING AN IMPACT

'AWESOME AS AN ARMY WITH BANNERS'

One type of banner mentioned in the Old Testament was apparently made of some sort of reflective material, mounted on poles, which caught the sunlight and presented a dazzling sight to the enemy. In today's praise processions the dazzling sight we need to display is the word of God.

Banners also serve to identify us, primarily as Christians, but also as Christians gathering together from many different churches. One of the exciting things about a praise procession is the way it unites Christians from different churches, as together we make a stand for Jesus, and for his truth and righteousness. The scriptures and phrases displayed

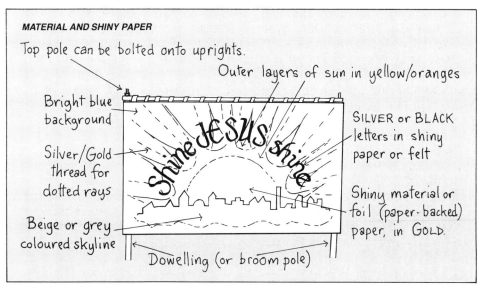

MATERIAL AND SHINY PAPER

Top pole can be bolted onto uprights.

Outer layers of sun in yellow/oranges

Bright blue background

SILVER or BLACK letters in shiny paper or felt

Silver/Gold thread for dotted rays

shine JESUS shine

Beige or grey coloured skyline

Shiny material or foil (paper-backed) paper, in GOLD.

Dowelling (or broom pole)

provide beauty and colour, bringing joy and life to our grey streets and creating an exciting spectacle to catch the attention of people passing by.

You may find the following hints helpful in making your banners:

(1) Remember that your banner will be viewed from a distance, so don't waste your time on fine detail.

(2) Unless well supported, large banners tend to crumple. Use plenty of battens and get some handy person to bracket corner joints. Bracket together pieces so that you are not trying to transport a fifteen-foot length of wood in an eleven-foot long car! Large banners also need a few carefully cut holes in them to allow the air to flow through when you are walking with them and to avoid being caught by the wind.

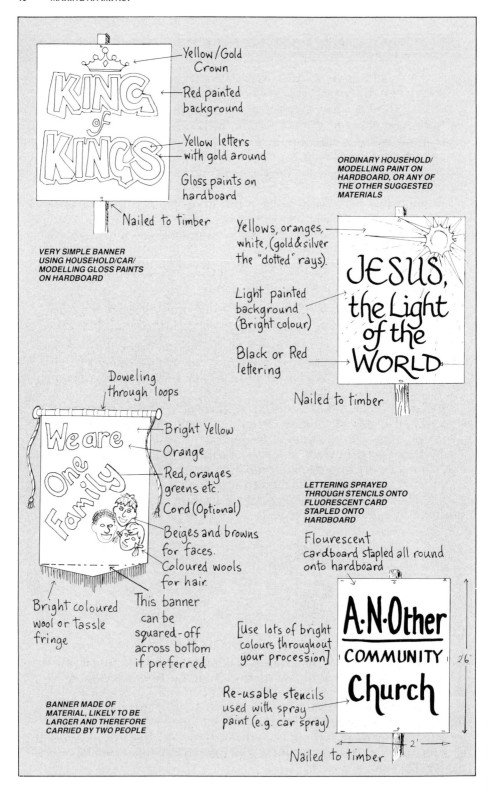

Yellow/Gold Crown

Red painted background

Yellow letters with gold around

Gloss paints on hardboard

Nailed to timber

VERY SIMPLE BANNER USING HOUSEHOLD/CAR/ MODELLING GLOSS PAINTS ON HARDBOARD

ORDINARY HOUSEHOLD/ MODELLING PAINT ON HARDBOARD, OR ANY OF THE OTHER SUGGESTED MATERIALS

Yellows, oranges, white, (gold & silver the "dotted" rays).

Light painted background (Bright colour)

Black or Red lettering

Nailed to timber

Doweling through loops

Bright Yellow

Orange

Red, oranges greens etc.

Cord (Optional)

Beiges and browns for faces. Coloured wools for hair.

Bright coloured wool or tassle fringe

This banner can be squared-off across bottom if preferred

[Use lots of bright colours throughout your procession]

BANNER MADE OF MATERIAL, LIKELY TO BE LARGER AND THEREFORE CARRIED BY TWO PEOPLE

LETTERING SPRAYED THROUGH STENCILS ONTO FLUORESCENT CARD STAPLED ONTO HARDBOARD

Flourescent cardboard stapled all round onto hardboard

Re-usable stencils used with spray paint (e.g. car spray)

Nailed to timber

(3) Gloss paint on hardboard is very effective, simple and quick to do, and won't run in the rain!

(4) Spray your banner with waterproof fixer (the type available for shower-proof coats) if you feel your banner needs protection against the elements. If it is very wet and you want your banner to survive, you will need to cover it with clear polythene.

(5) Fabric paint is an effective and quick method for painting designs and lettering onto material.

(6) Lower-case letters are easier to read from a distance than capitals.

(7) You may like to try 'Spraymount', a spray adhesive available from graphic and stationery shops. This is helpful in fastening letters quickly as you can reposition them if you put them in the wrong place.

(8) Flag-pole carriers (your local Boys' or Girls' Brigade should have some) may ease the strain on the arms.

(9) You may find ideas for designs in the line drawings from the *Good News Bible.* You need to obtain permission from the Bible Society.

Balloons also add colour to processions and can be held in bunches and handed out to passers-by, especially children. Fill them with helium so that they float. Balloons and t-shirts printed with slogans are available (see Appendix).

'Swizzles' can be made by taping strips of crêpe paper to garden sticks. Small flags can similarly be made using larger pieces of crêpe paper, perhaps with the words 'Hosanna' written on them.

Children will particularly enjoy these, although a little supervision may be necessary to prevent mortal injury!

Four metres of ribbon attached to a garden stick makes an effective swirling dancing aid. These need lots of space and are perhaps best used during a set dance when the procession is stationary.

CLOTHES

Dress the part. It is not much good making colourful banners if your marchers look as dull as a wet Sunday afternoon. Encourage them to wear bright colourful clothes. They needn't all look like walking rainbows, but just a splash of colour, like a bright scarf, makes a lot of difference. Why not have your own church logo printed on T-shirts, sweat-shirts, or even baseball caps? Make Way mailings give details of special sweat- shirts and T-shirts. Dancers can look very effective if all dressed in matching outfits.

Fancy dress. You don't necessarily want to look like a travelling circus, (even if people think you are!), but adding a touch of carnival atmosphere by fancy dress, especially clowns, gives the impression of people who are joyful and not afraid to have fun (for too long the caricature of the church has been exactly the opposite).

Use your discretion – if the prime aim of your march is spiritual warfare rather than witness, fancy dress will not be appropriate.

Members of drama groups could dress as characters portraying good, evil, greed, fear, love or sin. 'Perfect love' could have the job of chasing 'fear'! The characters could appear later in static street drama. Take care, however, to stay within the general discipline of the march.

OUTRIDERS

Make sure you have detailed a number of people gifted in personal evangelism to move along with the march, talking to passers-by, inviting them to meetings, offering them leaflets. If your outriders get left behind chatting, so much the better, but make sure you have plenty of others to replace them. Don't be surprised if people are prepared to receive prayer for physical, emotional and spiritual problems – after all, you have been praying for God's power to be released.

Outriders need to be people who:
— Are open to seeing God meet people's needs there and then.
— Are gifted in counselling (ie good listeners).
— Are able to communicate the Gospel in simple contemporary terms.
— Have a living testimony.
— Are equipped with literature for follow up, plus a pen and paper.

NB: This is not simply a job for those who cannot sing.

On a more light-hearted level, your clowns might like to give out balloons (with a message card attached), sweets or badges to passing children – even adults may not refuse!

LEAFLETS

People are nosey! They will be wondering:

Who are these strange people?
Are they a protest movement?
What have they got to sing about?
Why are they smiling?

Don't leave them guessing. Use a leaflet giving the following simple information:

1) Who you are, ie the name of your church/churches, not *just* 'a group of local Christians'.
2) What you believe (briefly) and what you've got to sing about.
3) An invitation to regular meetings, or a special event after the march.
4) An address and phone number for anyone who wants help, counsel or Christian literature, etc.

NB: The first and fourth pieces of information (except the phone number) are necessary by law, and must be accompanied by the words 'published by . . .' The maximum penalty for infringement is £25 per sheet distributed.

DANCE FOR A PRAISE MARCH

Then shall the maidens rejoice in the dance, and the young men and the old shall be merry. I will turn their mourning into joy.

Jer 31:13 (*Revised Standard Version*).

Dance isn't just for the professionals, it is something that everyone can be involved in to show the joy and excitement in knowing Jesus. So let's get rid of our inhibitions and give everything we've got in worship to the Lord.

The march as a whole needs to contain as much movement as possible, with people clapping, waving, dancing and showing that they are enjoying themselves. If you don't have a dance group already, try to get together a group of at least six people who could lead the other marchers in dance. They should also work out more intricate dances for themselves to do during particular songs.

It is important that the dance group is prepared spiritually as well as technically. They should recognise that dance is a very powerful form of spiritual warfare as they give physical expression to what they believe is happening spiritually. They in particular are proclaiming Jesus, not only with their spirit and soul but also with their body, which is very threatening to the enemy.

What to wear. Basically, clothes need to be bright and easy to move in, such as jogging suits. Jazz shoes are available from dance shops, but lightweight plimsoles are fine.

Dance routines – some ideas and starting points.

Jesus, He is the Light of the world. All the marchers can be involved in this dance. As the leader sings, simply walk to the beat of the music. As everyone starts to sing, continue walking and raise the right arm in front of you. The arm should be pointing straight up by the word 'world', 'peace' or 'God', and then lowered to the side. On the 'shout' phrase simply clap until the word 'Light', 'Prince' or 'Son' at which point both arms are raised straight up above the head in a sudden movement, and kept there until the phrase and movement repeat. These movements can be used for each verse.

Clear the road (*chorus only*). A minimum of four dancers is needed for this. Split them up into pairs, one pair placed six feet in front of the other one (this distance being maintained throughout the dance). The rear pair (B) runs past the front pair (A) to 'prepare the way of the Lord'. Pair A then performs the same movement during the next line. Pair B then repeats the movement again for the third line so that it ends up in front of pair A. Both A and B then turn on the spot to the last line 'of the Lord'.

The running movement begins with a small hop into the run. The body is curved forward and is straightened up as the arms sweep forward and then open above the head, falling naturally to the side. The hop and run starts on 'prepare' and the arms come down on 'Lord'. The pair that is not running forward walks in time with the music.

PASSING OPINION

'I think it's super.'

'It's different, very different – it's not really my cup of tea.'

'Rubbish.'

'They're singing in tune – that helps.'

'This sort of thing doesn't happen in Reading. Everybody's smiling – maybe they know something we don't. Everybody's just got big smiles on their faces. I never walk round Reading with a smile on my face, so maybe there's something I don't know.

FOLLOW-UP – Beware the 'Fizzle Factor'!

You march the streets, buoyed up with confidence, feeling like the mighty army the church was meant to be. You declare the power of Jesus, rejoice in His name – and then what?

You all go home!

This is what is known as the 'fizzle factor' and is to be avoided if possible. Your marchers are elated – they have discovered that it is not so embarrassing as they thought to have Aunty Flo and the milkman seeing them singing the praises of Jesus on the high street. The truths they have been proclaiming are ringing in their ears. There is a lot of potential energy waiting to be tapped.

HOW CAN YOU USE IT?

— Send people out in small groups to walk around the streets and pray for those areas.

— Have an open-air evangelistic rally at the end of the march.

— Set up several small open-air bases with street theatre, dance, testimonies, etc, and detail marchers to the different strategic points to pray, sing and witness.

— Send people out in small groups to give out leaflets in flats, shopping centres, etc.

— Have coffee ready at a hall near the end of the march and invite passers-by in.

— If you are fininshing in a park, get everyone to bring their sandwiches and end with a picnic.

— Plan a special evangelistic event for immediately afterwards, or in the evening.

— If processing to a park, invite people to join the procession on the way. Have banners to that effect – this is great for holiday towns in the summer when families are looking for something to do.

— Even if your marchers just disperse, remind them to be open to the Holy Spirit. Several people have commented how unusual opportunities to witness occurred just after the march due to the spiritual atmosphere having been changed.

In any case, Make Way should not be used as a one-off event, but as part of an ongoing strategy for evangelism (see chapter 8: Street-wise Evangelism.

Advice from the past:

'Experience taught that every outdoor service should if possible be connected with an indoor meeting – where, free from those dissipating influences which more or less always accompany outdoor preaching . . . the gospel could with greater clearness be set out.'

East London Christian Mission 1868
(forerunner of the Salvation Army)

STREET-WISE EVANGELISM

I have already suggested you can include a variety of ingredients in the procession programme. If you intend to end the march with an open-air meeting, or if you are performing Make Way statically in a shopping precinct, the following hints will help you know what to do and how to do it.

STRAIGHT PREACHING

Be succinct, and keep the presentation simple (two minutes).
— Make and emphasise one point clearly.
— Use short, catchy, pithy sentences.
— Be topical and relevant.
— Don't be offensive – share good news, not bad news.

OBJECT LESSONS

Jesus often applied spiritual truths from everyday items such as leaven, seeds, treasure or bread. Using familiar things to make a spiritual point attracts the attention of a passer-by and is more easily remembered than straight preaching.

SKETCHING AND LADDER WRITING

The street artist always attracts attention. Using the Open Air Campaigners' technique of 'painting with patter', there is time to put over Gospel truths while turning a simple ladder structure into words which visually communicates salient points.

PICTURES

For those with a little artistic ability, pictures mounted on cards work well on the street. Two or three pictures drawn in advance have a powerful visual impact. An alternative is to use a collage of newspaper or magazine cuttings.

ROLE PLAY OR DRAMA

Prophetic drama or role play was often used in the Old Testament, for example, Ezekiel lying in the street for 430 days. Modern equivalents can make an equally dramatic point, such as chaining your pastor to the railings to illustrate a person's need to be set free by Jesus. There are also many short sketches available for street drama.

LITERATURE TABLES

This can complement other types of open-air work or provide an alternative form of outreach. It provides free literature and a chance to chat. A large poster placed next to the table with a succinct immediate message can communicate as much as shouting with a megaphone.

TESTIMONIES

Interviewing an 'ordinary' Christian on the street can be less intimidating than a straight preach for both the interviewee and listener alike. Questions and answers can quickly get to the heart of the Gospel, using that person as the visual aid.

SOLOS, DUETS, TRIOS, ETC

The occasional performance song can add another powerful dynamic to the mix of items in an open-air presentation.

OTHER IDEAS

Puppets, banners, film shows (after dark), open-air services.

IMPRESSIONS O

'We were changed by the experience. We had started out as a rather nervous body of people prepared to make the right noises but still with some nervousness. We came back and would have marched all round again and much further had we been allowed to. We had been made bold.'

Wimbledon Praise March.

'It was raining, but we all got together to worship the Lord, singing the praises of God. As we sang, a woman (by this time windows were opened all around us) suddenly left her room and ran towards us saying, "The Lord has sent you."
The songs were inspired. As she heard them, God began ministering to her. "What a joy," she proclaimed, "God is here. You people have brought him to me – show how I can know him now." '

Broadwater Farm Estate, Tottenham.

'I found the Lord telling me to arrange a peaceful picket against the Occult Fayre using our group to sing praise. I didn't like the idea and told God so. But after we had prayed, I mentioned the idea to my friend. He said, "Oh, you too!" At that point, as we looked at one another in somewhat incredulous amazement, someone else walked up the aisle and told our vicar that he hoped to arrange a peaceful picket outside the civic centre.
Well – OK, Lord!'

Bromley, Kent.

'Some of the people marching with us the second time had responded to the Lord through our first Make Way march – Hallelujah! We intend to keep on "snowballing" for the Lord, gathering up more folks on the way.'

Preston, Lancast

STREET PRAISE

'I shall never forget the sight of every one of our 200 marchers dancing wildly to a Hebrew folk tune in the middle of a busy Welsh town square. Quiet ministers, old ladies, young lads – all praising God for Jesus. Abergavenny has never seen anything like it!'

Abergavenny, South Wales.

'Anglicans? Singing on the street? No minister? (Yes, that's him doing the shouting.) You aren't collecting money? It's very good. At least 800 people actually stopped to watch and listen. Many more heard it as they went about their business. The following morning at the service about thirty people became Christians.'

Bomaderry, Australia.

'A man who was standing on the other side of the road and had been watching, broke down in tears and got saved there and then.'

Watford, Hertfordshire.

'The police escort ensured a safe journey cross busy roads back to the New Life Centre where nothing could hold us back from lively, liberated praise. The expressions on the faces of the two young policemen who had been invited back to coffee were priceless!'

Brighton, Sussex.

MAKE WAY!

SHINE, JESUS, SHINE – SONGS FOR THE STREETS

IN MARCH ORDER

Prepare the way
  (Clear the road)
Cry hosanna
Fling wide your doors
Jesus, He is the Light of the world
Raise the shout!
Creation creed
  (The Lord is a mighty King)

The King of glory comes
  (King of kings)
Lord, have mercy on this nation
I will build My church
God is good/Dance, dance, dance/
  Cry hosanna (reprise)
Light has dawned
Shine, Jesus, shine (reprise)

(Please refer to *The Graham Kendrick Songbook* Vol 2 for
the music for MAKE WAY! – A CARNIVAL OF PRAISE)

FANFARE

SHOUT

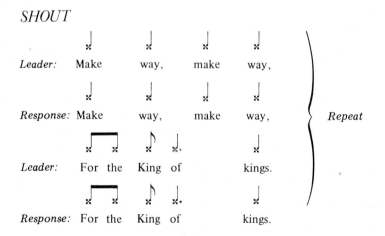

Prepare the way
(Clear the road)

4 VERSES WITH CHORUSES;
REPEAT FINAL CHORUS

Capo 2 (C)

Graham Kendrick

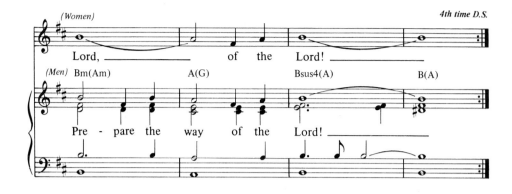

2. Raise Your voice and join the song,   *(echo)*
   God made flesh to us has come.   *(echo)*
   Welcome Him, your banners wave.   *(echo)*
   (Cheers, shouts, wave banners, etc.)

3. For all sin the price is paid,   *(echo)*
   All our sins on Jesus laid.   *(echo)*
   By His blood we are made clean.   *(echo)*
   (Cheers, shouts of thanksgiving)

4. At His feet come humbly bow,   *(echo)*
   In your lives enthrone Him now.   *(echo)*
   See, your great Deliverer comes.   *(echo)*
   (Cheers, shouts welcoming Jesus)

(Chorus twice to end)

SHOUT

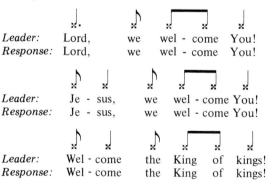

Leader: Lord,   we   wel - come   You!
Response: Lord,   we   wel - come   You!

Leader: Je - sus,   we   wel - come You!
Response: Je - sus,   we   wel - come You!

Leader: Wel - come   the   King   of   kings!
Response: Wel - come   the   King   of   kings!

All: *Cheers, etc.*

Cry hosanna

Capo 2 (C)

Graham Kendrick

Fling wide your doors

*TWICE; 3rd TIME
THROUGH TO CODA*

Graham Kendrick

All: Great and wonderful are Your deeds,
O Lord God the Almighty,
Just and true are Your ways,
O King of the nations!
Who shall not honour and praise Your name, O Lord?
For You alone are holy;
All nations shall come and worship in Your presence,
For Your righteous acts have been revealed.
To Him who sits on the throne
And to the Lamb
Be praise,
And honour,
Glory and might,
For ever and ever,
Amen!

Jesus, He is the Light of the world

Graham Kendrick

Raise the shout!

Graham Kendrick

SHOUT

All: Your kingdom come, Your will be done, ⎫
Here on the earth, as it is in heaven. ⎭ *Repeat*

Creation creed
(The Lord is a mighty King)

2 VERSES WITH CHORUSES;
REPEAT FINAL CHORUS

Capo 2 (G)

Graham Kendrick

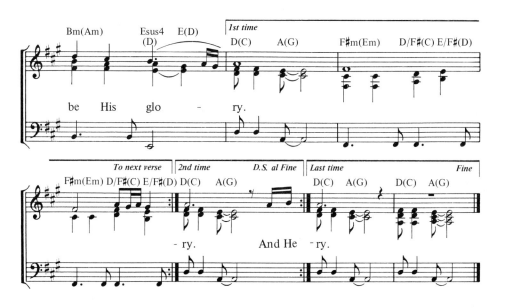

2. And yet we were deceived,   *(Men)*
   In pride the Lie believed,   *(Women)*
   To sin and death's decay —   *(Men)*
   The whole creation fell that day. *(Women)*
   Now all creation   *(Men)*
   Yearns for liberation;   *(Women)*
   All things in Christ restored —   *(Men)*
   The purchase of His precious blood. *(Women)*

   (Chorus twice to end)

SHOUT

All: For by Him
         All things were created,
         Things in heaven
         And on earth,
         Visible and invisible,
         Whether thrones
         Or powers
         Or rulers
         Or authorities;
         All things were created by Him,
         And for Him.

The King of glory comes
(King of kings)

TWICE THROUGH

Graham Kendrick

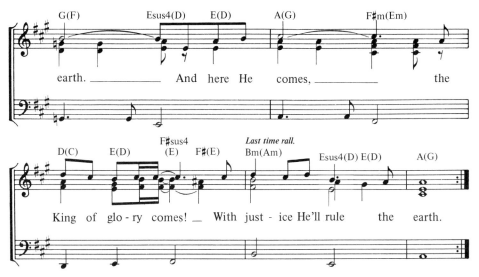

(Last time: Cheers, shouts of victory, etc.)

SHOUT

All: Almighty God, You are the Rock;
All Your works are perfect,
And all Your ways are just.
You are a faithful God who does no wrong.
Yet we Your people,
Both church and nation,
Are covered with shame
Because of our unfaithfulness to You.
We have sinned so seriously against You,
And against one another –
Therefore the foundations of our society crumble.
Have mercy, Lord,
Forgive us, Lord,
Restore us, Lord,
Revive Your church again;
Let justice flow
Like rivers,
And righteousness like a never-failing stream.

Lord, have mercy on this nation

TWICE THROUGH VERSE; CHORUS; VERSE; CHORUS

Graham Kendrick

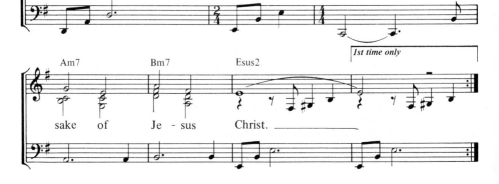

Lord, have mer - cy on this na - tion, for the sake of Je - sus Christ.

SHOUT

Leader:	Now Lord, send Your Holy Spirit.
Response:	Now Lord, send Your Holy Spirit.
Leader:	Drench this land with Your awesome presence.
Response:	Drench this land with Your awesome presence.
Leader:	Send Your Holy Spirit more powerfully.
Response:	Send Your Holy Spirit more powerfully.
Leader:	Let grace and mercy flood this land.
Response:	Let grace and mercy flood this land.
Leader:	Let mercy triumph over judgement.
Response:	Let mercy triumph over judgement.

} *(Repeat)*

I will build My church

TWICE THROUGH

Graham Kendrick

God is good / Dance, dance, dance / Cry hosanna (reprise)

Graham Kendrick

Leader: Who has power to save?
Response: (Clap x4) Je - sus!

Leader: Who has power to heal?
Response: (Clap x4) Jesus!
Leader: Who has conquered death?
Response: (Clap x4) Jesus!
Leader: Who is Lord of all?
Response: (Clap x4) Jesus!

Light has dawned

4 VERSES WITH CHORUSES
REPEAT FINAL CHORUS

Capo 2 (G)

Graham Kendrick

(Women)
2. Saviour of the world is He,
    Heaven's King come down.
    Judgement, love and mercy meet
    At His thorny crown.

(Men)
3. Life has sprung from hearts of stone,
    By the Spirit's breath.
    Hell shall let her captives go,
    Life has conquered death.

4. Blood has flowed that cleanses from sin,
    God His love has proved.
    Men may mock and demons may rage,
    We shall not be moved!

(Chorus twice to end.)

Shine, Jesus, shine (reprise)

Capo 2 (G)

Graham Kendrick

N.B. *A longer ending to this song can be found on the recording, and more accomplished musicians or larger musical groups may wish to use that as an appropriate ending to their march.*

MAKE WAY!

SHINE, JESUS, SHINE – SONGS FOR THE STREETS

ARRANGEMENTS FOR INSTRUMENTS

The following arrangements are based on those on side two of the *Shine, Jesus, Shine* cassette, LP and CD, although somewhat simplified for non-professional players. They can be used together with the piano arrangements in the previous section, and are deliberately designed for easy use in the open air.

These parts are intended for you to apply to your own situation, whatever the range of instruments and abilities. The arrangements are designed to work for most combinations of instruments, with an emphasis on the brass ensemble – a particularly effective sound in the open air – as the basic unit. Flute can double at the octave, while oboe and clarinet can be played in unison and saxophones can double various parts. Try out different voicings for yourself and assess the best effects. Do bear in mind that some instruments, such as saxophones which are transposing, may need to have their parts written out in the key in which they are playing rather than in concert as they are written here.

All songs by Graham Kendrick
Arranged by Christopher Norton

PREPARE THE WAY

CRY HOSANNA

FLING WIDE YOUR DOORS

JESUS, HE IS THE LIGHT OF THE WORLD

RAISE THE SHOUT!

CREATION CREED

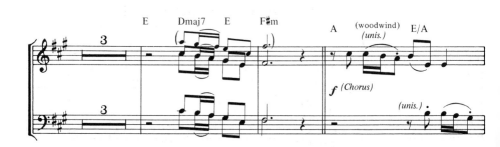

THE KING OF GLORY COMES

LORD HAVE MERCY ON THIS NATION

I WILL BUILD MY CHURCH

GOD IS GOOD   DANCE, DANCE, DANCE

CRY HOSANNA (reprise)

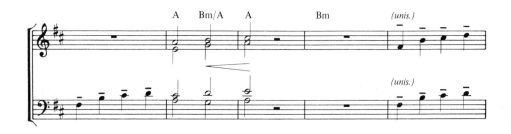

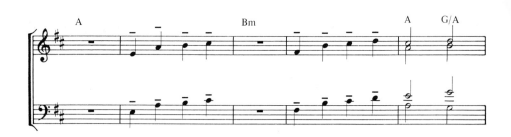

LIGHT HAS DAWNED

SHINE JESUS SHINE (reprise)

MAKE WAY!

COMBINED SONGS OF WORSHIP & PRAYER

IN ALPHABETICAL ORDER

from *MAKE WAY! – SHINE, JESUS SHINE* and *MAKE WAY! – A CARNIVAL OF PRAISE*

For this purpose

Capo 2(C)

Flowing

Intro.

Graham Kendrick

1. For this pur - pose Christ was re - veal'd to de - stroy all the works of the Ev - il One. Christ in us has ov - er -

2. In the name of Jesus we stand,
    By the power of His blood
    We now claim this ground.
    Satan has no authority here,
    Powers of darkness must flee,
    For Christ has the victory.

I worship You, O Lamb of God

Capo 2(D)

Graham Kendrick

2. I kneel before the Lamb of God . . . (etc.)

Lord, the light of Your love
(Shine, Jesus, shine)

Capo 2(G)

Graham Kendrick

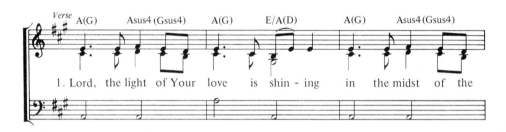

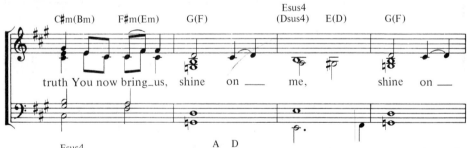

2. Lord, I come to Your awesome presence,
   From the shadows into Your radiance;
   By the blood I may enter Your brightness,
   Search me, try me, consume all my darkness.
   Shine on me, shine on me.

3. As we gaze on Your kingly brightness
   So our faces display Your likeness,
   Ever changing from glory to glory,
   Mirrored here may our lives tell Your story.
   Shine on me, shine on me.

(Chorus twice to end.)

O Lord, the clouds are gathering

N.B. Some congregations may find this song more comfortable to sing in a slightly lower key, e.g. B major.

Graham Kendrick

2. O Lord, over the nations now
    Where is the dove of peace?
    Her wings are broken.
    O Lord, while precious children starve
    The tools of war increase;
    Their bread is stolen.

3. O Lord, dark powers are poised to flood
    Our streets with hate and fear;
    We must awaken!
    O Lord, let love reclaim the lives
    That sin would sweep away
    And let Your kingdom come.

4. Yet, O Lord, Your glorious cross shall tower
    Triumphant in this land,
    Evil confounding.
    Through the fire Your suffering church display
    The glories of her Christ:
    Praises resounding!

Show Your power, O Lord

Capo 2(G)

Graham Kendrick

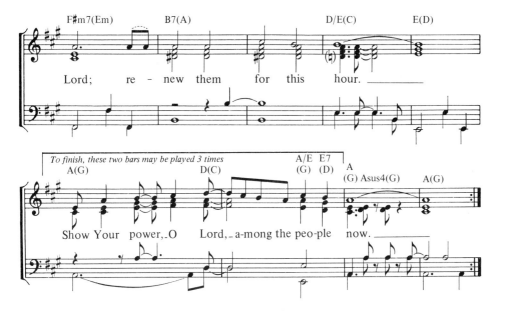

2. Show Your power, O Lord,
    Cause Your church to rise and take action.
    Let all fear be gone,
    Powers of the age to come
    Are breaking through.
    We Your people are ready to serve,
    To arise and to obey.
    Show Your power, O Lord,
    And set the people free.

    Ending last time
    Show Your power, O Lord,
    And set the people —
    Show Your power, O Lord,
    And set the people —
    Show Your power, O Lord,
    And set the people free.

Soften my heart

Graham Kendrick

Such love

Capo 4(C)

Graham Kendrick

2. Such love, stilling my restlessness;
   Such love, filling my emptiness;
   Such love, showing me holiness;
   O Jesus, such love.

3. Such love springs from eternity;
   Such love, streaming through history;
   Such love, fountain of life to me;
   O Jesus, such love.

We shall stand

Capo 3(D)

Graham Kendrick

1. Lord You have cho - sen me _ for _ fruit - ful - ness, _____
to be trans-formed _ in - to _ Your _ like
ness. _____ I'm gon-na fight on through _ 'till I see You _ face _
_ to _ face. _

2. Lord as Your witnesses
    You've appointed us.
    And with Your Holy Spirit
    Anointed us.
    And so I'll fight on through
    'Till I see You face to face.

Who can sound the depths of sorrow

Capo 1(A)

With feeling ♩= 106

Graham Kendrick

2. We have scorned the truth You gave us,
   We have bowed to other lords.
   We have sacrificed the children
   On the altars of our gods.
   O let truth again shine on us,
   Let Your holy fear descend:
   Upon our nation, upon our nation
   Have mercy Lord.

   (Men)
3. Who can stand before Your anger?
   Who can face Your piercing eyes?
   For You love the weak and helpless,
   And You hear the victims' cries.
   (All)
   Yes, You are a God of justice,
   And Your judgement surely comes:
   Upon our nation, upon our nation
   Have mercy, Lord.

   (Women)
4. Who will stand against the violence?
   Who will comfort those who mourn?
   In an age of cruel rejection,
   Who will build for love a home?
   (All)
   Come and shake us into action,
   Come and melt our hearts of stone:
   Upon Your people, upon Your people
   Have mercy, Lord.

5. Who can sound the depths of mercy
   In the Father heart of God?
   For there is a Man of sorrows
   Who for sinners shed His blood.
   He can heal the wounds of nations,
   He can wash the guilty clean:
   Because of Jesus, because of Jesus
   Have mercy, Lord.

*N.B. Some congregations may wish to add to the effectiveness of this song
   by transposing the final verse up a semitone, into B major.*

MAKE WAY!

SHINE, JESUS, SHINE – SONGS FOR THE STREETS

IN MARCH ORDER

SHOUT

Ldr: Make way, make way
All: Make way, make way

Ldr: For the King of kings
All: For the King of kings

Ldr: Make way, make way
All: Make way, make way

Ldr: For the King of kings
All: For the King of kings

All: *(Cheer!)*

CLEAR THE ROAD make wide the
  way, *(Men)*
Clear the road make wide the
  way. *(Women)*
Welcome now the God who
  saves, *(Men)*
Welcome now the God who
  saves. *(Women)*
Fill the streets with shouts
  of joy. *(Men)*
Fill the streets with shouts
  of joy. *(Women)*

(Cheers, eg Hallelujah! God is with us!
Love has conquered! Thank you Lord!
Welcome Lord!)*

Prepare the way of the
  Lord, (Men)
Prepare the way of the
  Lord, (Women)
Prepare the way of the Lord, (Men)
  of the Lord. (Women)

Raise your voice and join the
  song, *(Men)*
Raise your voice and join the
  song. *(Women)*
God made flesh to us has
  come, *(Men)*
God made flesh to us has
  come. *(Women)*
Welcome Him your banners
  wave, *(Men)*
Welcome Him your banners
  wave. *(Women)*

(Wave banners, cheers, eg
  Welcome Jesus!
Reign King Jesus! Jesus—the
  Conqueror!)*

For all sin the price is paid, *(Men)*
For all sin the price is paid. *(Women)*
All our sins on Jesus laid, *(Men)*
All our sins on Jesus laid. *(Women)*
By His blood we are made
  clean, *(Men)*
By His blood we are made
  clean. *(Women)*

(Cheers, eg Thank you Lord! I'm
  forgiven!
Hallelujah! Jesus—Saviour of
  the world!)*

MAKE
WAY

At His feet come humbly bow,   *(Men)*
At His feet come humbly
    bow,   *(Women)*
In your lives enthrone Him
    now.   *(Men)*
In your lives enthrone Him
    now.   *(Women)*
See, your great Deliverer
    comes.   *(Men)*
See, your great Deliverer
    comes.   *(Women)*

(Cheers, eg Come Lord Jesus!
    Jesus is Lord!
Jesus, Deliverer! King of Kings!
    Lord of Lords!)

(Chorus twice to end)

Graham Kendrick.
Copyright © Make Way Music/Thankyou Music 1988.

SHOUT

Ldr: Lord, we welcome You!
All: Lord, we welcome You!

Ldr: Jesus, we welcome You!
All: Jesus, we welcome You!

Ldr: Welcome the King of kings!
All: Welcome the King of kings!

All: *(Cheers, etc)*

CRY HOSANNA,   *(Men)*
Cry hosanna.   *(Women)*
Wave your banners,   *(Men)*
Wave your banners.   *(Women)*
Cry hosanna,   *(Men)*
Cry hosanna.   *(Women)*
Sing, sing, sing.   *(All)*

(Repeat)

Graham Kendrick.
Copyright © Make Way Music/Thankyou Music 1988.

FLING WIDE YOUR DOORS, *O you*
    streets,
Open up you hearts of men,
That the King of glory may come in.
Fling wide your doors, O you
    streets,
Open up you hearts of men,
That the King of glory may come in.

Who is this King of glory?   *(Women)*
The Lord, strong and mighty.   *(Men)*
Who is this King, this King of
    glory?   *(Women)*
The Lord, His name is Jesus!   *(Men)*

*(Sequence: Chorus, Verse, Chorus,
    Verse, Chorus)*

Ldr: Fling wide your doors
All: Fling wide your doors

Ldr: O you streets
All: O you streets

All: Open up you hearts of men

Ldr: Fling wide your doors
All: Fling wide your doors

Ldr: O you streets
All: O you streets

All: Open up you hearts of men

All: *(Cheers, shouts, etc during
    and at end of instrumental)*

Graham Kendrick.
Copyright © Make Way Music/Thankyou Music 1988.

SHOUT

All: Great and wonderful are
    Your deeds
    O Lord God the Almighty,
    Just and true are Your ways
    O King of the nations.
    Who shall not honour and praise
    Your name, O Lord?
    For you alone are holy.
    All nations shall come and
    worship in Your presence,
    For Your righteous acts have
    been revealed.
    To Him who sits on the throne
    And to the Lamb
    Be praise
    And honour
    Glory and might
    For ever and ever
    Amen!

Ldr (Sings): **JESUS, HE IS THE LIGHT
    OF THE WORLD.**
    Everyone sing,

All (Sing): Jesus, He is the Light
    of the world.
Ldr (Shout): Everyone shout!
All (Shout): Jesus! The Light of the
    world.
    Jesus! The Light of the
    world.

Ldr (Sings): Jesus, He is the Prince
    of peace.
    Everyone sing,
All (Sing): Jesus, He is the Prince of
    peace.
Ldr (Shout): Everyone shout!
All (Shout): Jesus! The Prince of
    peace!
    Jesus! The Prince of
    peace!

Ldr (Sings): Jesus, He is the Son
    of God.
    Everyone sing,
All (Sing): Jesus, He is the Son
    of God.
Ldr (Shout): Everyone shout!
All (Shout): Jesus! The Son of God!
    Jesus! The Son of God!

Graham Kendrick.
Copyright © Make Way Music/Thankyou Music 1988.

Ldr: **RAISE THE SHOUT!**
All: Jesus reigns!
Ldr: Shout it out!
All: Jesus reigns!
    Christ the fight did win,
    Smashed the power of sin,
    Love has broken in among us.

Ldr: Raise the shout!
All: Jesus lives!
Ldr: Shout it out!
All: Jesus lives!
    He burst from the grave,
    Now has power to save
    All who put their trust in Him.

Graham Kendrick.
Copyright © Make Way Music/Thankyou Music 1988.

(All)
And He made us for His delight,
Gave us the gift of life,
Created us family,
To be His glory,
To be His glory.

And yet we were deceived   *(Men)*
To pride the Lie believed   *(Women)*
To sin and death's decay—   *(Men)*
The whole creation fell that
   day.   *(Women)*
Now all creation   *(Men)*
Yearns for liberation;   *(Women)*
All things in Christ restored—   *(Men)*
The purchase of His precious
   blood.   *(Women)*

(Chorus twice to end)

Graham Kendrick.
Copyright © Make Way Music/Thankyou Music 1988.

SHOUT

All: Your kingdom come,
    Your will be done,
    Here on the earth,
    As it is in heaven.
    Your kingdom come,
    Your will be done,
    Here on the earth,
    As it is in heaven.

SHOUT

All: For by Him
    All things were created,
    Things in heaven
    And on earth,
    Visible and invisible,
    Whether thrones
    Or powers
    Or rulers
    Or authorities;
    All things were created by Him
    And for Him.

THE LORD IS A MIGHTY KING,   *(Men)*
The Maker of everything.   *(Women)*
The Lord He made the earth,   *(Men)*
He spoke, and it came at once to
   birth.   *(Women)*
He said, 'Let Us make mankind,'   *(Men)*
The crown of His design,   *(Women)*
'In Our own likeness,'   *(Men)*
His image in every human
   face.   *(Women)*

KING OF KINGS, Lord of lords,
Lion of Judah, Word of God.
King of kings, Lord of lords,
Lion of Judah, Word of God.

And here He comes, the King of glory
  comes!
In righteousness He comes to judge
  the earth.
And here He comes, the King of glory
  comes!
With justice He'll rule the earth.

(Repeat from King of kings)

All: (Cheers, shouts of victory, etc)

Graham Kendrick.
Copyright © Make Way Music/Thankyou Music 1988.

SHOUT

All: Almighty God, You are the Rock;
         All Your works are perfect
         And all Your ways are just.
         You are a faithful God who does
           no wrong.
         Yet we Your people,
         Both church and nation,
         Are covered with shame
         Because of our unfaithfulness
           to You.
         We have sinned so seriously
           against You,
         And against one another—
         Therefore the foundations of
           our society crumble.
         Have mercy, Lord,
         Forgive us, Lord,
         Restore us, Lord,
         Revive Your church again;
         Let justice flow
         Like rivers,
         And righteousness like a
           never-failing stream.

**LORD, HAVE MERCY
ON THIS NATION,**
For the sake of Jesus Christ.
  (Repeat—First time only)
Cleanse us, heal us, save us,
For the sake of Jesus Christ.

(Repeat from Lord have mercy)

Graham Kendrick.
Copyright © Make Way Music/Thankyou Music 1988.

SHOUT

Ldr: Now, Lord, send Your Holy
         Spirit.
All: Now, Lord, send Your Holy
         Spirit.

Ldr: Drench this land with Your
         awesome presence.

All: Drench this land with Your
         awesome presence.

Ldr: Send Your Holy Spirit more
         powerfully.
All: Send Your Holy Spirit more
         powerfully.

Ldr: Let grace and mercy flood this
         land.
All: Let grace and mercy flood this
         land.

Ldr: Let mercy triumph over
         judgement.
All: Let mercy triumph over
         judgement.

Ldr: Let mercy triumph over
         judgement.
All: Let mercy triumph over
         judgement.

MAKE
WAY

I WILL BUILD MY CHURCH, *(Men)*
I will build My church, *(Women)*
And the gates of hell *(Men)*
And the gates of hell *(Women)*
Shall not prevail *(Men)*
Shall not prevail *(Women)*
Against it. *(All)*

(Repeat)

So you powers in the heavens above,
    bow down!
And you powers on the earth below,
    bow down!
And acknowledge that Jesus,
Jesus, Jesus, is Lord, is Lord.

(Repeat from I will build my church)

Graham Kendrick.
Copyright © Make Way Music/Thankyou Music 1988.

GOD IS GOOD, *we sing and*
    shout it,
God is good, we celebrate.
God is good, no more we doubt it,
God is good, we know it's true.

And when I think of His love for me,
My heart fills with praise
And I feel like dancing.
For in His heart there is room for me
And I run with arms open wide.

(Repeat chorus only)

Graham Kendrick.
Copyright © Make Way Music/Thankyou Music 1985.

DANCE, DANCE, DANCE,
His truth has set us free.
Sing, sing, sing,
His song of liberty.
Dance, dance, dance,
His truth has set us free.
Sing, sing, sing,
His song of liberty.

Graham Kendrick.
Copyright © Make Way Music/Thankyou Music 1988.

CRY HOSANNA, *(Men)*
Cry hosanna, *(Women)*
Wave your banners, *(Men)*
Wave your banners, *(Women)*
Cry hosanna, *(Men)*
Cry hosanna. *(Women)*
Sing, sing, sing, *(All)*
    (Last time only)
Sing!

(Repeat)

Graham Kendrick.
Copyright © Make Way Music/Thankyou Music 1988.

SHOUT

Ldr: Who has power to save?

All: *(Clap × 4)* Jesus!

Ldr: Who has power to heal?
All: *(Clap × 4)* Jesus!

Ldr: Who has conquered death?
All: *(Clap × 4)* Jesus!

Ldr: Who is Lord of all?
All: *(Clap × 4)* Jesus!

LIGHT HAS DAWNED that ever shall blaze,
Darkness flees away.
Christ the light has shone in our hearts,
Turning night to day.

We proclaim Him King of kings,
We lift high His name.
Heaven and earth shall bow at His feet
When He comes to reign.

(Women only)
Saviour of the world is He,
Heaven's King come down.
Judgement, love and mercy meet
At His thorny crown.

(Men only)
Life has sprung from hearts of stone,
By the Spirit's breath.
Hell shall let her captives go,
Life has conquered death.

(All)
Blood has flowed that cleanses from sin,
God His love has proved.
Men may mock and demons may rage,
We shall not be moved!

(Chorus twice to end)

Graham Kendrick.
Copyright © Make Way Music/Thankyou Music 1988.

SHINE, JESUS, SHINE,
Fill this land with the Father's glory;
Blaze, Spirit, blaze,
Set our hearts on fire.
Flow, river, flow,
Flood the nations with grace and mercy;
Send forth Your word,
Lord, and let there be light.
   (Last time)
Let there be light.

(Repeat)

(All cheer and clap, etc)

Graham Kendrick.
Copyright © Make Way Music/Thankyou Music 1987.

MAKE WAY!

A CARNIVAL OF PRAISE – SONGS FOR THE STREETS

IN MARCH ORDER

SHOUT

Ldr: Make way, make way
All: Make way, make way

Ldr: For the King of kings
All: For the King of kings

Ldr: Make way, make way
All: Make way, make way

Ldr: For the King of kings
All: For the King of kings

MAKE WAY, MAKE WAY, for Christ
  the King
In splendour arrives.
Fling wide the gates and welcome Him
Into your lives.

> *Make way,* (Men)
>   *make way,* (Women)
> *Make way,* (Men)
>   *make way,* (Women)
> *For the King of kings.* (Men)
> *For the King of kings.* (Women)
> *Make way,* (Men)
>   *make way,* (Women)
> *Make way,* (Men)
>   *make way,* (Women)
> *And let His kingdom in.* (All)

He comes the broken hearts to heal
The prisoners to free.
The deaf shall hear, the lame shall
  dance,
The blind shall see.

And those who mourn with heavy
  hearts,
Who weep and sigh;
With laughter, joy and royal crown
He'll beautify.

We call you now to worship Him
As Lord of all.
To have no gods before Him
Their thrones must fall!

(Chorus twice to end)

Graham Kendrick.
Copyright © Make Way Music/Thankyou Music 1986.

MAKE
WAY

WE DECLARE *that the kingdom of*
    God is here.   (Men)
We declare that the kingdom of
    God is here.   (Women)
We declare that the kingdom of
    God is here.   (Men)
We declare that the kingdom of
    God is here.   (Women)
Among you,   (Men)
    among you.   (Women)
Among you,   (Men)
    among you.   (Women)

    (Last time only)

We declare that the kingdom of
    God is here.   (Men)
We declare that the kingdom of
    God is here.   (Women)
We declare that the   (Men)
Kingdom of God is here.   (All)

The blind see, the deaf hear, the lame
    men are walking,
Sicknesses flee at His voice.
The dead live again, and the poor
    hear the good news:
Jesus is King, so rejoice!

(Sequence: Chorus twice, Verse,
    Chorus, Verse, Chorus twice)

Graham Kendrick.
Copyright © Make Way Music/Thankyou Music 1986.

SHOUT

♩ ♪ ♫

Ldr: Let God arise
All: Let God arise

♪ ♪ ♪ ♪ ♪ ♪♪ ♪♪

Ldr: And let His enemies be scattered
All: And let His enemies be scattered

Ldr: Let God arise
All: Let God arise

Ldr: And let His enemies be scattered
All: And let His enemies be scattered

LET GOD ARISE,
And let His enemies be scattered;
And let those who hate Him
Flee before Him.
Let God arise,
And let His enemies be scattered;
And let those who hate Him
Flee away.

But let the righteous be glad,   *(Men)*
The righteous be glad,   *(Women)*
Let them exult before God,   *(Men)*
Let them exult before God,   *(Women)*
Let them rejoice with gladness,   *(Men)*
O let them rejoice,   *(Women)*
Building up a highway for the
    King,   *(Men)*
For the King,   *(Women)*
We go in the name of the Lord,   *(Men)*
Let the shout go up   *(Men)*
In the name of the Lord.   *(All)*

Graham Kendrick.
Copyright © Make Way Music/Thankyou Music 1986.

MAKE WAY

THE EARTH IS THE LORD'S   (Men)

And ev'rything in it,   (Women)
The earth is the Lord's   (Men)
The work of His hands,   (Women)
The earth is the Lord's   (Men)
And ev'rything in it;   (Women)
And all things were made
For His glory   (All)

(Last time)

And all things were made,
Yes all things were made,
And all things were made
For His glory.

The mountains are His,
The seas and the islands,
The cities and towns,
The houses and streets.
Let rebels bow down
And worship before Him,
For all things were made
For His glory.

(Sequence: Chorus, Verse, Chorus,
Verse, Chorus twice)

Graham Kendrick.
Copyright © Make Way Music/Thankyou Music 1986.

WE BELIEVE in God the Father,
Maker of the universe,
And in Christ His Son our Saviour,
Come to us by virgin birth.
We believe He died to save us,
Bore our sins, was crucified.
Then from death He rose victorious,
Ascended to the Father's side.

Jesus, Lord of all, Lord of all,
Jesus, Lord of all, Lord of all,
Jesus, Lord of all, Lord of all,
Jesus, Lord of all, Lord of all.
Name above all names.
Name above all names.
   (Last time)
Name above all names.

We believe He sends His Spirit,
On His church with gifts of power.
God His word of truth affirming,
Sends us to the nations now.
He will come again in glory,
Judge the living and the dead.
Every knee shall bow before Him,
Then must every tongue confess.

Graham Kendrick.
Copyright © Make Way Music/Thankyou Music 1986.

MAKE WAY

SHOUT

Ldr: Shout for joy for the Lord

is good

All: Shout for joy for the Lord
is good

Ldr: He is just and true in all His ways
All: He is just and true in all His ways

Ldr: Shout for joy for the Lord
is good
All: Shout for joy for the Lord
is good

Ldr: He is just and true in all His ways
All: He is just and true in all His ways.

JESUS PUT THIS SONG into our
hearts,
Jesus put this song into our hearts,
It's a song of joy no one can take away,
Jesus put this song into our hearts.

Jesus taught us how to live in
harmony,
Jesus taught us how to live in
harmony,
Different faces, different races,
He made us one,
Jesus taught us how to live in
harmony.

Jesus taught us how to be a family,
Jesus taught us how to be a family.
Loving one another with the
Love that He gives,
Jesus taught us how to be a family.

Jesus turned our sorrow into dancing,
Jesus turned our sorrow into dancing,
Changed our tears of sadness into
Rivers of joy,
Jesus turned our sorrow into a dance.

(Instrumental)

Graham Kendrick.
Copyright © Make Way Music/Thankyou Music 1986.

SHOUT

All   Christ has died
three times:
          Christ has risen

          Christ will come again.

THE LORD IS MARCHING out in
  splendour,
In awesome majesty He rides,
For truth, humility and justice,
His mighty army fills the skies.

  O give thanks to the Lord
  For His love endures,
  O give thanks to the Lord
  For His love endures,
  O give thanks to the Lord
  For His love endures,
  For ever, for ever.
    (Last time)
  For ever.

His army marches out with dancing
For He has filled our hearts with joy.
Be glad the kingdom is advancing
The love of God, our battle cry!

(Chorus three times to end)

Graham Kendrick.
Copyright © Make Way Music/Thankyou Music 1986.

IN THE TOMB so cold they laid Him,
Death its victim claim'd.
Pow'rs of hell, they could not hold
  Him;
Back to life He came!

  Christ is risen!   (Men)
  Christ is risen!   (Women)
  Death has been conquer'd!   (Men)
  Death has been
    conquer'd!   (Women)
  Christ is risen!   (Men)
  Christ is risen!   (Women)
  He shall reign for ever.   (All)

Hell had spent its fury on Him,
Left Him crucified.
Yet by blood, He boldly conquered,
Sin and death defied.

Now the fear of death is broken,
Love has won the crown.
Pris'ners of the darkness listen,
Walls are tumbling down.

Raised from death to heaven
  ascending,
Love's exalted King.
Let His song of joy, unending,
Through the nations ring!

(Chorus twice to end)

Graham Kendrick.
Copyright © Make Way Music/Thankyou Music 1986.

MAKE
WAY

MAKE WAY!

COMBINED SONGS OF WORSHIP & PRAYER

IN ALPHABETICAL ORDER

1 Graham Kendrick.
Copyright © Make Way Music/
Thankyou Music 1986.

ALL HEAVEN WAITS with bated breath,
For saints on earth to pray.
Majestic angels ready stand
With swords of fiery blade.
Astounding power awaits a word
From God's resplendent throne.
But God awaits our pray'r of faith
That cries 'Your will be done.'

Awake, O church, arise and pray
Complaining words discard.
The Spirit comes to fill your mouth
With truth, His mighty sword.
Go place your feet on Satan's ground
And there proclaim Christ's name,
In step with heaven's armies march
To conquer and to reign!

Now in our hearts and on our lips
The word of faith is near,
Let heaven's will on earth be done,
Let heaven flow from here.
Come blend your prayers with Jesus' own
Before the Father's throne;
And as the incense clouds ascend
God's holy fire rains down.

Soon comes the day when with a shout
King Jesus shall appear.
And with Him all the church,
From every age, shall fill the air.
The brightness of His coming shall
Consume the lawless one,
As with a word the breath of God
Tears down His rebel throne.

One body here, by heav'n inspired,
We seek prophetic power;
In Christ agreed, one heart and voice,
To speak this day, this hour,
In every place where chaos rules
And evil forces brood;
Let Jesus' voice speak like the roar
Of a great multitude.

2 Graham Kendrick.
Copyright © Make Way Music/
Thankyou Music 1985.

FOR THIS PURPOSE Christ was revealed,
To destroy all the works
Of the Evil One.
Christ in us has overcome,
So with gladness we sing
And welcome His kingdom in.

> *Over sin He has conquered,* (Men)
> *Hallelujah, He has conquered.* (Women)
> *Over death victorious,* (Men)
> *Hallelujah, victorious.* (Women)
> *Over sickness He has triumphed,* (Men)
> *Hallelujah, He has triumphed.* (Women)
> *Jesus reigns over all!* (All)

In the name of Jesus we stand,
By the power of His blood
We now claim this ground.
Satan has no authority here,
Powers of darkness must flee,
For Christ has the victory.

3 Graham Kendrick.
Copyright © Make Way Music/
Thankyou Music 1986.

HE THAT IS IN US *is greater than he*
That is in the world.
He that is in us is greater than he
That is in the world.

Therefore I will sing and I will rejoice
For His Spirit lives in me.
Christ the Living One has overcome
And we share in His victory.

All the powers of death and hell and sin
Lie crushed beneath His feet
Jesus owns the Name above all names,
Crowned with honour and majesty.

MAKE
WAY

4   Graham Kendrick.
Copyright © Make Way Music/
Thankyou Music 1988.

I WORSHIP YOU,   *(Men)*
I worship You,   *(Women)*
O Lamb of God,   *(All)*
Who takes away   *(Men)*
Who takes away   *(Women)*
The sin of the world.   *(All)*

(Repeat)

    Alleluia, Alleluia,
    Alleluia, Alleluia.

I kneel before   *(Men)*
I kneel before   *(Women)*
The Lamb of God,   *(All)*
Who takes away   *(Men)*
Who takes away   *(Women)*
The sin of the world.   *(All)*

5   Graham Kendrick.
Copyright © Make Way Music/
Thankyou Music 1986.

LORD, HAVE MERCY ON US,
Come and heal our land.
Cleanse with Your fire,
Heal with Your touch.
Humbly we bow
And call upon You now.
O Lord, have mercy on us.
O Lord, have mercy on us.
   (Last time)
O Lord, have mercy on us.

6   Graham Kendrick.
Copyright © Make Way Music/
Thankyou Music 1987.

LORD, THE LIGHT OF YOUR LOVE is shining
In the midst of the darkness, shining;
Jesus, Light of the World, shine upon us,
Set us free by the truth You now bring us,
Shine on me, shine on me.

   Shine, Jesus, shine,
   Fill this land with the Father's glory;
   Blaze, Spirit, blaze,
   Set our hearts on fire.
   Flow, river, flow,
   Flood the nations with grace and mercy;
   Send forth Your word,
   Lord, and let there be light.

Lord, I come to Your awesome presence,
From the shadows into Your radiance;
By the blood I may enter Your brightness,
Search me, try me, consume all my darkness.
Shine on me, shine on me.

As we gaze on Your kingly brightness
So our faces display Your likeness.
Ever changing from glory to glory,
Mirrored here may our lives tell Your story.
Shine on me, shine on me.

(Chorus twice to end)

7   Graham Kendrick.
Copyright © Make Way Music/
Thankyou Music 1986.

LORD, YOU ARE SO PRECIOUS to me,
Lord, You are so precious to me
And I love You,
Yes, I love You
Because You first lov'd me.

Lord, You are so gracious to me,
Lord, You are so gracious to me
And I love You,
Yes, I love You
Because You first loved me.

8   Graham Kendrick.
Copyright © Make Way Music/
Thankyou Music 1986.

MAY THE FRAGRANCE of Jesus fill this
  place.   *(Men)*
May the fragrance of Jesus fill this place.
  (Women)
May the fragrance of Jesus fill this
  place.   *(Men)*
Lovely fragrance of Jesus,   *(Women)*
Rising from the sacrifice
Of lives laid down in adoration.   *(All)*

May the glory of Jesus fill His church.   *(Men)*
May the glory of Jesus fill His
  church.   *(Women)*
May the glory of Jesus fill His church.   *(Men)*
Radiant glory of Jesus,   *(Women)*
Shining from our faces
As we gaze in adoration.   *(All)*

MAKE WAY

May the beauty of Jesus fill my life.   *(Men)*
May the beauty of Jesus fill my life.   *(Women)*
May the beauty of Jesus fill my life.   *(Men)*
Perfect beauty of Jesus,   *(Women)*
Fill my thoughts, my words, my deeds,
My all I give in adoration.   *(All)*
Fill my thoughts, my words, my deeds,
My all I give in adoration,
My all I give in adoration.

9   Graham Kendrick.
Copyright © Make Way Music/
Thankyou Music 1986.

MEEKNESS AND MAJESTY,

Manhood and Deity,
In perfect harmony,
The Man who is God.
Lord of eternity
Dwells in humanity,
Kneels in humility
And washes our feet.

O what a mystery,
Meekness and majesty.
Bow down and worship
For this is your God,
This is your God.
(Last time)
This is your God

Father's pure radiance,
Perfect in innocence,
Yet learns obedience
To death on a cross.
Suffering to give us life,
Conquering through sacrifice,
And as they crucify
Prays: 'Father forgive.'

Wisdom unsearchable,
God the invisible,
Love indestructible
In frailty appears.
Lord of infinity,
Stooping so tenderly,
Lifts our humanity
To the heights of His throne.

10   Graham Kendrick.
Copyright © Make Way Music/
Thankyou Music 1987.

O LORD, THE CLOUDS ARE GATHERING,

The fire of judgement burns,
How we have fallen!
O Lord, You stand apall'd to see
Your laws of love so scorn'd,
And lives so broken.

Have mercy, Lord,   (Men)
Have mercy, Lord,   (Women)
Forgive us, Lord,   (Men)
Forgive us, Lord,   (Women)
Restore us, Lord,
Revive Your church again.
Let justice flow,   (Men)
Let justice flow,   (Women)
Like rivers,   (Men)
Like rivers,   (Women)
And righteousness
like a never failing stream
(Last time)
A never-failing stream.

O Lord, over the nations now
Where is the dove of peace?
Her wings are broken.
O Lord, while precious children starve
The tools of war increase;
Their bread is stolen.

O Lord, dark powers are poised to flood
Our streets with hate and fear;
We must awaken!
O Lord, let love reclaim the lives
That sin would sweep away
And let Your kingdom come.

Yet, O Lord, Your glorious cross shall tower
Triumphant in this land,
Evil confounding.
Through the fire Your suffering church display
The glories of her Christ:
Praises resounding!

(Chorus twice to end)

MAKE WAY

11   Graham Kendrick.
Copyright © Make Way Music/
Thankyou Music 1984.

O LORD, YOUR TENDERNESS,
Melting all my bitterness,
O Lord, I receive Your love.
O Lord, Your loveliness,
Changing all my ugliness,
O Lord, I receive Your love,
O Lord, I receive Your love,
O Lord, I receive Your love.

12   Graham Kendrick.
Copyright © Make Way Music/
Thankyou Music 1983.

REJOICE! REJOICE!
Christ is in you,
The hope of glory
In our hearts.
He lives! He lives!
His breath is in you,
Arise a mighty army,
We arise.

Now is the time for us
To march upon the land,
Into our hands
He will give the ground we claim.
He rides in majesty
To lead us into victory,
The world shall see
That Christ is Lord!

God is at work in us
His purpose to perform,
Building a kingdom
Of power not of words,
Where things impossible,
By faith shall be made possible;
Let's give the glory
To Him now.

Though we are weak, His grace
Is everything we need;
We're made of clay
But this treasure is within.
He turns our weaknesses
Into His opportunities,
So that the glory
Goes to Him.

13   Graham Kendrick.
Copyright © Make Way Music/
Thankyou Music 1988.

SHOW YOUR POWER, O LORD,
Demonstrate the justice of Your kingdom.
Prove Your mighty word,
Vindicate Your name
Before a watching world.
Awesome are Your deeds, O Lord;
Renew them for this hour.
Show Your power, O Lord,
Among the people now.

Show Your power, O Lord,
Cause Your church to rise and take action.
Let all fear be gone,
Powers of the age to come
Are breaking through.
We Your people are ready to serve,
To arise and to obey.
Show Your power, O Lord,
And set the people free.
    (Ending last time)
Show Your power, O Lord,
And set the people—
Show Your power, O Lord,
And set the people—
Show Your power, O Lord,
And set the people free.

14   Graham Kendrick.
Copyright © Make Way Music/
Thankyou Music 1988.

SOFTEN MY HEART, LORD,
Soften my heart,
From all indifference
Set me apart.
To feel Your compassion,
To weep with Your tears;
Come soften my heart, O Lord,
Soften my heart.

15   Graham Kendrick.
Copyright © Make Way Music/
Thankyou Music 1988.

SUCH LOVE, pure as the whitest snow;
Such love, weeps for the shame I know;
Such love, paying the debt I owe;
O Jesus, such love.

Such love, stilling my restlessness;
Such love, filling my emptiness;
Such love, showing me holiness;
O Jesus, such love.

Such love, springs from eternity;
Such love, streaming through history;
Such love, fountain of life to me;
O Jesus, such love.

16 Graham Kendrick.
Copyright © Make Way Music/
Thankyou Music 1988.

WE SHALL STAND
With our feet on the Rock.
Whatever men may say,
We'll lift Your Name up high.
And we shall walk
Through the darkest night.
Setting our faces like flint,
We'll walk into the light.

Lord, You have chosen me
For fruitfulness,
To be transformed into
Your likeness.
I'm gonna fight on through
'Till I see You, face to face.

Lord, as Your witnesses
You've appointed us.
And with Your Holy Spirit
Anointed us.
And so I'll fight on through,
'Till I see You, face to face.

(*To finish, repeat line* 'We shall stand'.
or 'We'll walk into the light')

17 Graham Kendrick.
Copyright © Make Way Music/
Thankyou Music 1988.

WHO CAN SOUND THE DEPTHS OF SORROW
In the Father heart of God,
For the children we've rejected,
For the lives so deeply scarred?
And each light that we've extinguished
Has brought darkness to our land,
Upon our nation, upon our nation,
Have mercy Lord.

We have scorned the truth You gave us,
We have bowed to other lords.
We have sacrificed the children
On the altars of our gods.
O let truth again shine on us,
Let Your holy fear descend.
Upon our nation, upon our nation,
Have mercy, Lord.

(Men only)
Who can stand before Your anger?
Who can face Your piercing eyes?
For You love the weak and helpless,
And You hear the victims' cries.
(All)
Yes, You are a God of justice,
And Your judgement surely comes.
Upon our nation, upon our nation,
Have mercy, Lord.

(Women only)
Who will stand against the violence?
Who will comfort those who mourn?
In an age of cruel rejection,
Who will build for love a home?
(All)
Come and shake us into action,
Come and melt our hearts of stone.
Upon Your people, upon Your people,
Have mercy, Lord.

Who can sound the depths of mercy
In the Father heart of God?
For there is a Man of sorrows
Who for sinners shed His blood.
He can heal the wounds of nations,
He can wash the guilty clean.
Because of Jesus, because of Jesus,
Have mercy, Lord.

MAKE
WAY

APPENDIX A: Additional shouts to be led by the leader

Here are some further shouts which may be used by the leader.

'ECHO' SHOUTS (*Marchers to echo the leader*)

Some of these are presented as a simple line, some in sets to be used as a sequence. Most of them can be used rhythmically.

Choose life – choose Jesus! (insert love, truth, hope, etc).

Hail – the King of kings!
Jesus – the King of kings!
Let His Kingdom come!
Let His will be done!

Glory and honour,
Power and strength,
Wealth and wisdom,
belong to Jesus!

The Kingdom is Yours! (or His)
The power is Yours!
The glory is Yours!
Now and for ever!

The Lord lives!
The Lord is just!
The Lord is good!
The Lord reigns for ever!

O taste and see that the Lord is good!

Give thanks to the Lord for His love endures for ever!

Great is the Lord and worthy of praise!

Prepare the way of the Lord!

Make way for Jesus!

Hallelujah! For the Lord our God the Almighty reigns!

Christ has died, Christ is risen, Christ will come again!

SPELLING SHOUTS

The leader can shout, 'Give us a "J",' after which all shout, 'J', etc spelling 'JESUS'. He can then ask 'What does it spell?' and other questions with the answer 'JESUS'. Similarly, use words like 'LOVE', 'HOPE', 'PEACE' etc followed by appropriate questions from the leader answered by that word, eg 'What does Jesus bring?' (Leader – write them down and practise beforehand to avoid getting in a muddle!)

CORPORATE DECLARATIONS, PRAYERS AND SCRIPTURES

For corporate reading led by the leader.

1. Yet for us there is but one God, the Father, from whom are all things, and we exist for Him, and there is One Lord, Jesus Christ, through whom are all things, and we exist through Him.

2. We affirm the triumphant power of love. Love that comes from God. Love that was revealed in Christ, God's Son. Love is patient, love is kind, love does not envy or boast. Love is not proud, or rude or self-seeking. Love is not short-tempered and keeps no record of wrongs. Love does not delight in evil, but rejoices with the truth. Love always protects, always trusts, always hopes and does not give up. Love never fails!

3. Love shall finally triumph, and Jesus, the King of love, shall reign forever!

4. O God our Creator, You have made us for Yourself, and our hearts are restless till they find their rest in You.

5. Turn from your sinful ways and be baptised, every one of you, in the name of Jesus Christ, for the forgiveness of your sins. And you will receive the gift of the Holy Spirit!

6. Let the sinner forsake his way and the evil man his thoughts. Let him turn to the Lord, and He will have mercy on him, and to our God for He will freely forgive!

7. Restore us O God, make Your face shine upon us, that we may be saved!

8. In the name of Jesus we stand, by the power of His blood we now claim this ground. Satan has no authority here, powers of darkness must flee, for Christ has the victory!

9. Jesus said: 'I have come that you might have life, and have it in all its fulness'. (Further texts beginning 'Jesus said' may be suitable.)

10. Holy, Holy, Holy is the Lord God, the Almighty, who was, and is, and is to come!

11. All authority, glory and sovereign power belong to You O Lord! All

peoples, nations and men of every language will worship You! Your dominion will be an everlasting dominion, it will not pass away. Your kingdom will not be destroyed– Hallelujah!

12. Now to the King eternal, immortal, invisible, the only God, be honour and glory for ever and ever, amen!

13. You were declared with power to be the Son of God by the resurrection from the dead, according to the Spirit of holiness – Jesus Christ our Lord!

14. 'In the last days,' says the Lord, 'I will pour out My Spirit on all people. Your sons and daughters will prophesy, your old men will dream dreams, your young men will see visions. Even on My servants, both men and women, I will pour out My Spirit in those days.'

15.   For God loved the world so much, that He gave His only Son, that whoever believes in Him should not die, but have everlasting life.

APPENDIX B: A note about the Marchers' Handbook

The Make Way Marchers' Handbook contains the following:

INTRODUCTION

ON YOUR MARKS . . .!
In the weeks leading up to the march.

GET SET . . .!
Pre-march checklist.

GO . . .!

AT THE END . . . Beware the the 'Fizzle Factor'!

MAKE WAY! – SHINE, JESUS, SHINE
SONGS FOR THE STREETS
Complete lyrics, calls and responses (*in march order*).

MAKE WAY! – A CARNIVAL OF PRAISE
SONGS FOR THE STREETS
Complete lyrics, calls and responses (*in march order*).

MAKE WAY! – SHINE, JESUS, SHINE
MAKE WAY! – A CARNIVAL OF PRAISE
COMBINED SONGS OF WORSHIP AND PRAYER
(*in alphabetical order by first line*).

APPENDIX A: Additional shouts to be led by the leader.

APPENDIX B: Some useful items and addresses.

APPENDIX C: Guitar chord charts

The following chord diagrams show the fingering for the guitar chords in this songbook.

Key

o = *play open string*   2 = *index finger*   5 = *little finger*
x = *don't play string*   3 = *middle finger*   = *index finger bar*
1 = *thumb*   4 = *ring finger*   **3** = *fret number*

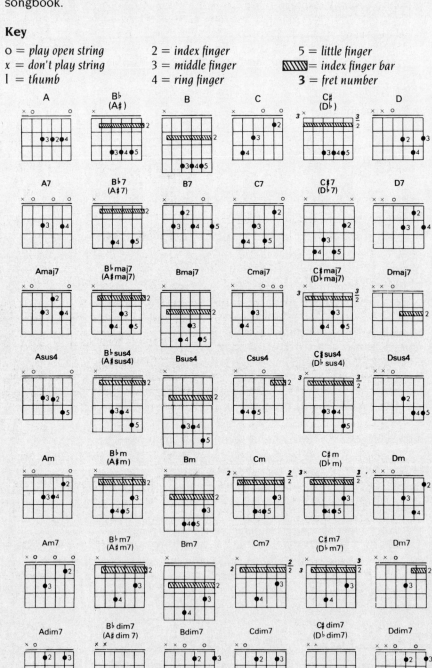

The chords which have been used throughout the book have been carefully chosen with the elementary guitarist in mind. Capo markings, in the left hand corner of many of the songs, allow simple chord shapes to be played with a capo in position. *Capo* 3 (C), for example, means place the capo at the third fret and play the simple chords in brackets, which you will find are in C rather than E♭. If you use these capo markings you will find that you are able to play almost all of the songs using just ten chords: C, D, Dm, E, Em, F, G, A, Am, B7. If you do see a chord which you don't know, you will probably find that it is playable by mentally stripping it of all its 'extras' e.g. Gmaj7, just play G; Dm9, just play Dm; Csus4, just play C.

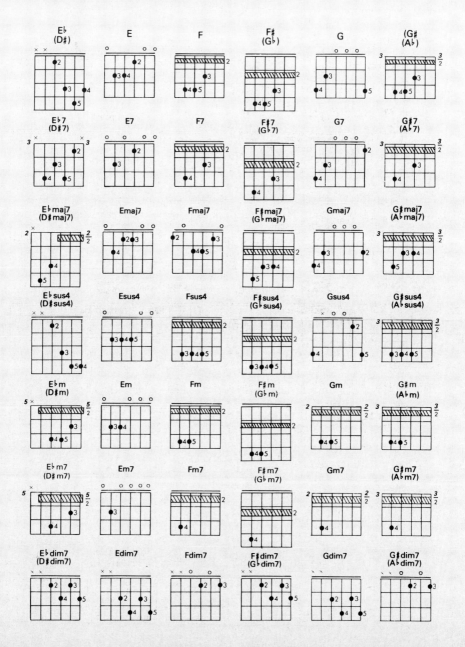

More unusual chords

In this songbook you will come across some more unusual chords – mainly chords with different bass notes. If you see D/A, for example, this means play the chord of D with the note A in the bass. For a guitarist who is strumming, this bass note isn't too important and he can just play an ordinary chord of D, but the A bass note is useful for bass and keyboard players, and for guitarists who are picking and want to add colour to their playing.

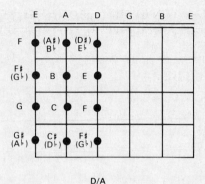

D/A

The diagram on the right above shows the position of bass notes on the guitar for those who want to learn them. Looking at the diagram you can work out that a D/A is simple (see second diagram).

As already stated, when *strumming*, the bass note (as long as it is a note from the chord) isn't too important as it doesn't sound above the other guitar strings. Because one requires as loud and full a sound as possible when strumming it is best to play chords which use all six strings. This can be achieved by incorporating a different bass note. Use the following full sounding versions of common chords when strumming. For –

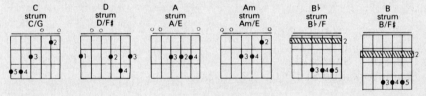

The following are the few more complex chords you will find in the songbook:

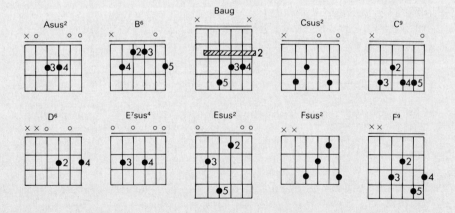

APPENDIX D: Some useful items and addresses

Your Church and the Media, a workbook by Nigel Sharp. Available from:

Christian Communication
45 Victoria Road
Swindon, Wilts SN1 2AY
Tel: (0793) 34314

Ocarina music and information available from:

Ocarina Workshop
68 St Mary's Road
Kettering, Northants NN15 7BW
Tel: (0536) 81547

Make Way video and audio ministry tapes on related subjects by Roger Forster. For sale or hire contact:

Ichthus Tape Ministry
116 Perry Vale
Forest Hill, London SE23 2LQ
Tel: 01-699 4208

For details of transpositions for brass instruments, and individual instrumental and vocal arrangements for most of the songs in the *Songs of Fellowship* range, contact:

The Songs of Fellowship
   Arrangement Service
P.O. Box 4, Sheffield
South Yorkshire S1 1DU

For details of special *Make Way* balloons and T-shirts, the *Make Way* ocarina package, or for any information concerning *Make Way*, contact:

Make Way Music Ltd
107-113 Stanstead Road
Forest Hill, London SE23 1HH
Tel: 01-699 7755

❝I have a growing conviction that if the church is to break new ground for the Kingdom of God, it is vital that we take praise and worship out of the 'cocoon' of our buildings and on to the housing estates, high streets, shopping precincts and village greens where the people are and where the powers of darkness rule through fear, gloom or apathy.❞

GRAHAM KENDRICK

❝I want to fill the world with the music of heaven – the music that shall be the herald of salvation, the handmaiden of holiness, the trumpet call to duty, the evangel of Christianity and the servant of the Living God.❞

WILLIAM BOOTH

MAKE WAY! — A CARNIVAL OF PRAISE
LP SFR134, Cassette SFC134, Price £6.25 each.

MAKE WAY! — SHINE, JESUS, SHINE
LP SFR176, Cassette SFC176, Price £6.25 each; **CD SFC176**, Price £9.99.
The latest 'Make Way' recording complete with explanatory handbooks for organisers, musicians and marchers.

Graham Kendrick's

MAKE WAY
Handbooks

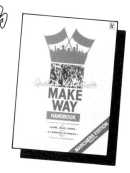

These handbooks together form an essential resource for all those considering 'Make Way' style processions on the streets.

MAKE WAY HANDBOOK Organiser's Guide & Music Edition Price £4.95

All you need to know about taking prayer, praise and witness on to the streets. What, where and how to do it, obtaining permission, policing, administration, advice to musicians, banner and dance ideas, etc.

Contains simple piano and guitar arrangements for MAKE WAY! – SHINE, JESUS, SHINE, including calls and responses and extra instrumentation for a street band in flexible format.

Note: The music for MAKE WAY! – A CARNIVAL OF PRAISE can be found in *The Graham Kendrick Songbook Vol 2*.

Also features a words-only section containing complete lyrics, calls and responses and songs of worship and prayer for MAKE WAY! – SHINE, JESUS, SHINE and MAKE WAY! – A CARNIVAL OF PRAISE.

MAKE WAY HANDBOOK Marchers' (Words-only) Edition Price £1.25.

Contains complete lyrics, calls and responses and songs of worship and prayer for MAKE WAY! – SHINE, JESUS, SHINE and MAKE WAY! – A CARNIVAL OF PRAISE.

Also includes instructions on how to make the most of the opportunities on the day.

Order from your usual Christian book and record supplier or direct from Make Way Music, 107-113 Stanstead Road, Forest Hill, London SE23 1HH.

THE *Graham Kendrick*
SONGBOOK Vol. 1

38 worship songs including 'Battle hymn', 'For this purpose', God is good', 'Jesus stand among us', 'Let God arise', 'Rejoice', Restore O Lord' and 'The Servant King', plus others from the albums *Let God Arise* and *Magnificent Warrior*.

Fully scored for piano with guitar chords, plus index.

Price £3.75

THE *Graham Kendrick*
SONGBOOK Vol. 2

Price £4.95

This companion volume to *The Graham Kendrick Songbook Vol. 1* is a unique selection of songs encompassing the broad range of Graham's music ministry.

★ Make Way — all the street-procession songs from the highly acclaimed *Make Way! – A Carnival of Praise*.

★ Praise & Worship — including 'If My people who bear My name', 'Lord, the light of Your love', 'O Lord, the clouds are gathering', and songs from the albums *Make Way! – A Carnival of Praise*, *Let God Arise*, *The King Is Among Us* and *Jesus Stand Among Us*.

★ Children's Songs — simple yet effective worship songs for children.

★ Concert Classics — a collection of songs taken from Graham's ministry in contemporary music.

Fully scored for piano with guitar chords, plus contents listing and full index.

All 2-page songs on facing pages to avoid turning over.

Order from your usual Christian book and record supplier or direct from:
Make Way Music, 107-113 Stanstead Road, Forest Hill, London SE23 1HH.

MAKE WAY

MAKE WAY MATERIALS

All the materials mentioned in this publication, plus other useful resources to assist in public witness can be ordered via the Make Way Music Office. Please send a stamped, self-addressed envelope for full details and an order form to Make Way Music, 107-113 Stanstead Road, Forest Hill, London SE23 1HH. All the profits from materials purchased in this way will be used to support the ministry of Graham Kendrick and his team.

Now also available: SHINE, JESUS, SHINE video, and OCARINA SONGBOOK.

MAKE WAY NEWSLETTER

If you want to keep in touch with news and developments of *Make Way* and other aspects of Graham Kendrick's ministry, a *MAKE WAY* newsletter is regularly incorporated into *WORSHIP* magazine. In addition to the newsletter, *WORSHIP* magazine, which is published quarterly, contains many features and articles of interest to all who are involved in praise and worship. The annual subscription is currently £3.00 and if you would like to subscribe, please use the coupon below (or a photocopy).

WORSHIP MAGAZINE (incorporating MAKE WAY NEWS) Subscription coupon.

Please send .... copy(ies) of *WORSHIP* quarterly, commencing with the current issue. I enclose a cheque for £ .... (@ £3.00 per subscription) made payable to the Christian Music Association, in respect of the first year's subscription.

Name ....

Address ....

....

.... Postcode ....

Post to: Christian Music Association, Glyndley Manor, Stone Cross, Eastbourne, East Sussex BN24 5BS.

IMPORTANT MESSAGE TO MARCH ORGANISERS

Performance permission

Graham is happy for Make Way Music to waive any performing right fee in most situations when *Make Way! – A Carnival of Praise* or *Make Way! – Shine, Jesus, Shine* is used on the streets. However, it is still essential to obtain written permission in advance from the Make Way office upon each occasion. We will gladly provide this free of charge if you send us a completed copy of the form below together with a stamped, self-addressed envelope. You may, if you prefer, send a completed photocopy of this form rather than use the original, should you wish to keep this form as a blank for future occasions.

Your co-operation with this will greatly assist Graham in his continuing preparation of music and resources for this kind of public witness. Graham would also appreciate your news of how you have used *Make Way*, together with any photographs, new ideas, etc.

Although there is no charge for this service, we would appreciate a contribution to help towards our administrative costs.

DATE OF EVENT .... **TITLE OF EVENT** ....

BRIEF DESCRIPTION OF EVENT ....

....

LOCATION OF EVENT ....

ORGANISING GROUP/COMMITTEE ....

ORGANISERS NAME ....

ADDRESS ....

.... **POSTCODE** ....

TELEPHONE NUMBER ....

APPROX NUMBER OF PEOPLE EXPECTED ....

Please attach a separate list of participating churches/groups, and a separate form for each event (if more than one). Please send this form together with any contribution (payable to MAKE WAY MUSIC) and a stamped, self-addressed envelope, to:

MAKE WAY MUSIC, 107-113 Stanstead Road, Forest Hill, London SE23 1HH.

IMPORTANT: This waiver offer does not otherwise affect the legal copyright in these songs. In all other circumstances all usual copyright and performing right procedures will apply.